Uncle Arthur's

BEDTIME STORIES

VOLUME FOUR

SHOSTAL

Uncle Arthur's

BEDTIME STORIES

VOLUME FOUR

BY
ARTHUR S. MAXWELL

PACIFIC PRESS PUBLISHING ASSOCIATION
Mountain View, California

H. BAERG

H. BAER

CONTENTS

Lesson Index

Artists participating in the illustration of this volume are Robert Berran, Harry Baerg, Siegfried Bohlmann, Kreigh Collins, Thomas Dunbebin, Harvey Fuller, John Gourley, Arlo Greer, Russell Harlan, Manning de V. Lee, Jeanie McCoy, Don Nelson, Vernon Nye, Herbert Rudeen, and Elmo White.

Teresina

O h, this wretched needle!" exclaimed Dorothy. "It simply won't thread."

"Never mind," said Sylvia, sewing away gaily, "think of Christmas, when all the dresses will be finished, and we can take Marguerita and Roxana out in their new carriage."

"And Teresina," said Dorothy. "She will have to have the best place. Do you know, I don't believe there ever has been a doll so beautiful as my Teresina. She has such lovely hair. And her face is so pretty I could just keep on kissing it."

"Yes," agreed Sylvia, "she is very beautiful. You are lucky to have her. I wish Auntie would send me one like that."

Teresina listened carefully from her seat on the floor, and felt very much pleased with herself.

"You know," added Dorothy, "one reason I can't stand that Kitty Larson is that she will pass remarks about Teresina when I see her."

"What can you expect?" said Sylvia. "Her people are very poor. What has she said to you lately?"

"Oh, nothing much, but she makes me mad. Why, you

9

Dorothy and Sylvia enjoyed a happy time together mending their dolls' clothes.

remember that it started to rain when I was shopping yesterday? Well, she happened to pass, and said to a girl she was with, 'If that were my doll, I would look after it better than that!' Just as though I don't look after my dolls! I wish she would just mind her own business and love her own dolls."

"I don't see how she can," said Sylvia, "poor, dirty, one-legged little things. I'd throw them in the garbage can if they were mine."

"So would I," said Dorothy.

Just then they heard the front door bang.

"Must be Mother coming back," said Sylvia.

It was, and a few moments later Mother burst into the room, all excitement.

10

"Oh, girls!" she said, collapsing into a chair, "we nearly lost Baby Brother just now."

"Why, whatever happened?" cried both together.

"I was crossing Princess Street, pushing the baby in his cart, when someone cried, 'Look out!' and I stopped still right in the middle of the road. A car swerved round us, skidded, and knocked down a child. I do feel dreadful about it."

"Poor Mother!" said Sylvia, "you must lie down at once and rest."

"Perhaps I'd better," said Mother. "Look after Baby Brother, won't you? and put him to bed."

The girls agreed, and Mother went to her room for a rest.

All thought of dolls and dresses was driven out of the girls' minds by this exciting news. How glad they were that Baby Brother had not been hurt! Poor Teresina felt quite put out when she saw the way they cuddled him.

"I do hope the child that saved you isn't badly hurt, Baby dear," said Sylvia.

"I hope he isn't," said Dorothy. "And imagine this happening just before Christmas. How sad!"

Early the next morning Mother started off to the hospital to find out how the child was getting on. She was gone a long time, and the girls began to wonder what could have happened to her. They were watching

11

for her out of the window and were just beginning to get anxious when footsteps were heard coming up the garden path.

"I've been to the hospital, and I've been around to see the child's mother," she began.

"Is he badly hurt?"

"Not very; and it is not a boy, but a little girl. She has a bad cut on her head, but will be all right again in a few days. She says she was so afraid Baby would be killed that she forgot all about herself and just shouted for all she was worth."

"What's her name?" asked Sylvia.

"I think she said it was Catherine," said Mother.

"What a name!" said Dorothy.

"Never mind," said Mother, "she is a good little girl, and you should see her home! We really must do something for them. There are several children, and the Father is out of work. They don't seem to have any money, and the poor Mother just broke down and cried when we talked about this new trouble."

"What can we do for them?" asked Sylvia.

"I've done one thing already," said Mother.

"What's that?" asked the girls together.

"Why, when the poor Mother told me how things were with her, and that she couldn't hope to give her children anything for

12

Christmas, I invited them all up here to a party."

"What a good idea, Mother!" said the girls.

"Yes, and I told the little girl that she could invite half a dozen of her best friends as well. So we shall have a lively time."

"I should think we shall," said Dorothy. "And we must get things ready for them—presents and bags of candy and nuts and fruit, you know."

"And couldn't Daddy dress up as Santa?" asked Sylvia.

"That would be splendid," said Mother. "I think we shall have a wonderful time. And shall we pack a nice big basket for them for Christmas morning?"

"Oh, let's do!" said Sylvia. "I should love to help get it ready."

And so the preparations began. There was not much time before the party, which was to take place two days before Christmas. Dorothy and Sylvia began making a list of presents they would need, and, oh, what joy they had looking for them in the stores! Of course, Mother had to help a good deal with the money, but they put in some themselves out of their own savings boxes. As the days passed, they became more and more excited about it and thought of all sorts of things they might do for their poor little guests.

"You know," said Sylvia one evening, "I've been wondering whether we shouldn't give away Marguerita and Roxana to two of the little girls."

"It would be dreadfully hard," said Dorothy, "but I think I should like to do it. Of course, I wouldn't think of giving Teresina away. I couldn't think of that."

"Oh, no," said Sylvia. "But we could make Marguerita

13

and Roxana two special presents."

"I will if you will," said Dorothy.

"All right," said Sylvia and the gifts were planned.

Meanwhile the little girl was discharged from the hospital. Returning to her home, she found her brothers and sisters very excited over the wonderful invitation that had been given them. Of course, they all did their best to make themselves as clean and tidy as possible for the great occasion. The little girl herself went around to six of her best friends, and told them to get ready to go along too. In every case it came as a great surprise, because they all belonged to quite poor homes, and it had seemed there wasn't going to be any special fun at all this Christmas.

At last the great evening arrived. A car picked up all the poor children, and it was a gay little company inside on the way up to the house where the party was to be held. Mother was on the doorstep ready to greet them, and she gave a specially tight hug to the little girl with the bandage round her head, leading her to her place at the big table.

Dorothy and Sylvia were still upstairs dressing when the

14

children arrived, but they soon came running down, to see what their little guests were like. They shook hands all around, giving the children a very jolly welcome.

"But where's the little girl that saved Baby Brother?" asked Sylvia.

"In the dining room with Mother," said someone.

Dorothy and Sylvia rushed in with all the other children

15

at their heels. The girl with the bandage was at the other end of the room.

Suddenly they stopped.

"It can't be— It can't be," whispered Dorothy to Sylvia.

"It is; I'm sure it is," whispered Sylvia. "But we must make her welcome."

"Come, girls," called Mother, "do come and speak to the little girl who——"

She did not finish, for the girls had now recognized one another.

"If it isn't Kitty Larson!" said Dorothy out loud. "Why, Mother, we have often seen her before. And you never told us that this was the little girl! I thought you said her name was Catherine."

"So it is," said the little girl. "But everyone calls me Kitty."

"Well, we're so glad you are here," said Sylvia, "and thank you for shouting just in time to save Baby, and perhaps Mother, too."

16

Then they started eating, and what rollicking fun they all enjoyed while it was going on! The poor children had never had such a good time in their lives before.

The only person who did not seem to be enjoying herself

very much was Dorothy. Presently she quietly left the table and went into another room for a few moments. When she returned she was looking much happier.

Quickly the evening passed. At last there came a loud knock at the door, the lights were turned down, and in came "Santa Claus" with a big bag of presents over his back. What shrieks of delight as he began to pass around the lovely gifts that Dorothy and Sylvia had prepared!

"Now," said Santa Claus, as he took the one last bulky package out of his bag and began to open it, "this is a special present for a special little girl. Will Kitty Larson please stand up?"

Kitty stood and her eyes opened wide.

"Stop him!" whispered Sylvia to Dorothy. "There's been a mistake. Stop him before it's too late."

"No, it's all right," said Dorothy. "I simply couldn't help it. I changed them just now during supper."

They were interrupted by Kitty.

"Oh, thank you, thank you ever so much," she said. "Can you really spare her?"

"She is yours, with all our love," said Dorothy with a brave smile, though she felt like weeping bucketfuls of tears.

It was her own precious Teresina.

"A Little Child Shall Lead Them"

You may think this is a made-up story, but it isn't. It is absolutely true. I know the little boy and girl it concerns very well indeed, and it was their mamma who told it to me.

Of course the names are not real. I couldn't tell you the real names, could I? So I will call the boy Donald and the girl Margaret. Margaret was five and Donald eight and a half.

It so happened that one day when Mamma was clearing up the dining room she threw an old Christmas card on the fire. It was a very old one that had been sent to Margaret at least four years before.

Hardly was it alight, however, when Margaret began to make a fuss.

"That's my Christmas card," she cried. "You shouldn't have burned it. I've kept it all this time, and I want it."

"But it was such a dirty card," said Mamma, trying to make the matter right. "And it has been lying about the place for such a long time I thought you did not want it any more."

"But of course I wanted it," cried Margaret, getting more angry. "You should have known I wanted it. Why should you burn my things, anyway?"

Mamma tried calmly to explain to Margaret that she had lots of other cards, that all together they were of no real value, and that very soon there would be another Christmas, when

PAINTING BY RUSSELL HARLAN

her friends probably would be sending her many more.

But Margaret refused to be reasoned with, and began calling her mamma some very naughty names. Whereupon Mamma tried another method of helping her little daughter —and the neighbors must have wondered what was happening next door. Just what happened I will leave you to guess, but I can tell you that very shortly afterward a sobbing little girl was getting in between a pair of sheets upstairs.

Donald was in bed by now also, and when Mamma had kissed them both good night and gone out of the room, he began to talk. Mamma, on the stairs, stopped to listen.

"Margaret," said Donald, "you must be a good girl and go fast asleep."

"I can't go to sleep," said Margaret. "I've been so naughty, and I don't want Mamma to spank me any more."

"Yes, dearie," said Donald, with sympathy and wisdom beyond his years, "you have been very naughty, and it made me feel so sad and ill inside, but if you would just say a little prayer all for yourself, it would make everything all right."

"But I don't know what to say," said Margaret, amid the tears and sobs that shook her little body.

"If you like, Margaret, I will help you," said Donald, "and you could say it after me. Shall I?"

"Yes, please."

There was a pause. Then Donald began:

"Dear Lord Jesus. Now Margaret, do, please."

"Dear Lord Jesus," repeated Margaret.

"Help me not to be naughty," said Donald.

"Help me not to be naughty," repeated Margaret.

"Forgive me for showing a naughty temper tonight," said Donald, firmly.

The sobs increased, and for a while Margaret did not speak.

"But you must say it," Donald insisted.

At last Margaret repeated, "Forgive me for showing a naughty temper tonight."

"And make me a good little girlie," continued Donald.

"And make me a good little girlie," repeated Margaret.

"And please wash all my sins away, for Jesus Christ's sake. Amen," said Donald.

Margaret again repeated after him.

"Is that all now, Donald?" she asked.

"Yes, dear," said Donald; "don't cry any more now. You know, the sheet you've spoiled in your book in heaven—where the angels write all that we do—has now been smudged all over with something like red, *ever so red,* crayon, and it has hidden all the writing about your naughty tricks, and no one can ever read about them again. That's just what Jesus does when we are sorry and ask Him to forgive us. Aren't you pleased, Margaret?"

"Oh, yes, Donald. I feel better now. And Mommy won't spank me any more?"

"No, Margaret, course not. You've asked Jesus to make you good, and if we're good, Mom and Dad are happy, and then they never have to spank us, do they?"

"No," said Margaret.

"Good night," said Donald.

"Good night, Donald," said Margaret. "I'm so glad it's all right now."

Then silence, while Mamma crept softly downstairs with tears in her eyes and gladness in her heart, happy to know that her darlings had already found a friend in Jesus, and were learning so soon to roll their burden upon the Lord.

23

Tom's Thoughtlessness

School was closed for the afternoon and Tom was spending the free time with some of his friends in the park.

They had all brought their lunch, and after playing tag and many other games, they sat down under a fine old oak tree to enjoy the good things their mothers had packed for them.

Soon they had finished, and for want of something better to do, they began throwing the banana skins and orange peels at one another, and scattering their lunch papers all over the place.

All of a sudden from behind the oak tree came an elderly gentleman. He made as if to go past the boys, but stepping on one of the banana skins, he fell heavily to the ground.

Tom sprang to his side in a moment and did his best to help him to his feet again.

"I hope you're not hurt, sir," he said.

"I think not," said the gentleman. "Just a little shaken. I think I will sit on the bench for a little while if I may. I must rest a few minutes."

24

Tom helped him across to the bench, and the boys stood around to see whether the gentleman had hurt himself.

"I think I'm all right," he said, "but I'm getting old now, and a fall like that is dangerous for one of my age. It's too bad that people are so careless with their banana skins, isn't it?"

"Yes," said Tom, but with a rather guilty look at the other boys.

"I hope you boys never throw banana skins about."

"Um," said Tom, blushing a little.

"So selfish, isn't it?" went on the elderly gentleman.

"I suppose it is," said Tom.

"If people only thought of the pain they might cause others, I'm sure they would never do it."

"No," said Tom.

"And look at all that paper lying about," said the elderly gentleman. "Some lazy, thoughtless people must have been here recently."

"Yes," said Tom, for there was nothing else he could say.

"If only," went on the gentleman, "if only people would stop to think about others, they would never leave a mess like this behind them, would they?"

"No," said Tom, getting more uncomfortable.

"You know," said the gentleman, "this is a beautiful park, but if everyone left a mess like this, it wouldn't be worth coming to. If it were all covered with dirty paper and orange peels and banana skins, why, you boys wouldn't want to play here, would you?"

"No, sir," said Tom and the rest together.

"Well, boys, I'm feeling better now. Thank you for helping me up. I'll be off again, I think. Here's something for you, son, to get some candy."

And so saying, to Tom's amazement, he handed him a quarter and walked away.

The boys looked at one another.

"I thought he was going to scold us," said one.

"He didn't see us," said another.

"Don't you believe it," said Tom. "I believe he saw everything we did."

"Anyhow, he was a good sport," said a third.

26

"And I liked what he said," said Tom. "He was very kind about it."

"You're right," said another. "And that's the last time I'm going to throw stuff around here."

"I feel the same way," said Tom, and so saying he began to pick up some of the litter he had so carelessly scattered a little while before. Strangely enough, the other boys got the same idea. They didn't say much to one another while they were doing it, but within a few minutes all the banana skins, orange peels and lunch papers had been picked up and dropped into one of the park trash cans.

"Well," said Tom, as he led the others off to the candy shop to spend his quarter, "I don't think we'll litter up this place again."

"I guess we won't!" chorused the others.

And sure enough, they didn't.

Feeding the Animals

Do you like to feed birds and animals? What great fun it is, isn't it?

And you may be very sure that the animals like it just as much. How Fido does jump about when you talk about dog biscuits! How pussy will purr when you pour out her saucerful of milk!

Then, of course, there are the chickens in the back yard. Don't they run when they see you coming with their food!

And there's that robin redbreast who comes and sits on the fence opposite the back door, waiting for the crumbs he hopes you are going to throw out. Doesn't he look excited and pleased!

Of course, you have been down to the pond sometimes to feed the ducks or the baby swans. Everyone likes throwing pieces of bread to them. How quickly the ducks gobble it all up and quack loudly for more!

Have you ever seen little woolly lambs feeding from a bottle? The children in our picture seem to be enjoying giving their pets some breakfast, don't they? One of the lambs wags

29

Did you ever try to feed a lamb from a bottle like this? It surely is fun.

his tail as though to say "Thank you," and one kneels as though to say "Please." The children must have taught them good manners.

If you are fortunate enough to live near a zoo, you have probably enjoyed feeding the animals there many times. What a noise the lions do make just before feeding time, don't they? But I think the sea lions make more still. And how they do jump when the keeper comes along with his pail of fish! Splash!

they go into the water, trying to be first to get the food. Rather greedy of them, isn't it?

Surely you have fed the monkeys, haven't you? Don't they love peanuts? And the bears, how they love bread! I once saw a big white polar bear at a zoo sit bolt upright, open his mouth in a broad smile, and actually wave his right paw at me— all to persuade me to throw him another piece of bread.

Giraffes are very particular about their food; perhaps because it has such a long way to go down their throats. But they like to have children feed them, nevertheless. So do the elephants, big as they are. Try putting a peanut in front of Mr. Elephant's trunk, and see what happens. You are in for a surprise.

Feeding helps so much in making wild animals tame. A big game hunter once caught a tiger in a trap. He wanted to bring it home alive. For the first few hours of the trip the captive animal made a terrible fuss, rushing about his cage and roaring terribly. Then as he discovered that his food came to him regularly without any trouble, he began to quiet down, and at last became quite docile.

Of course, it is possible to feed animals too much. Like boys and girls, they get indigestion if they overeat. Many a good dog has been spoiled because his youthful master has tried to show his affection for him by feeding him at all hours of the day and night.

On the other hand, it often happens that our pets are forgotten and left to go hungry because we are too busy to think about them. Have you ever forgotten to give your dog his supper? or come back late in the evening to remember that your chickens have gone to roost without their evening meal? Have

31

you ever left the rabbit hungry because you were playing football, and didn't think about it?

Well, if you have, it's too bad. How would you like to go to bed cold and hungry, or be told on coming in from school at noon that Mamma has been so busy reading a book, she has neglected to get your dinner ready? You wouldn't like it a bit, I know.

We should treat our faithful animal friends as we would like to be treated ourselves. I think the golden rule applies to them as well as to us, don't you? Certainly if we follow it we shall discover new sources of happiness and gather round us a host of loyal and devoted friends who will make life ever more interesting and beautiful day by day.

Those Gooseberries

Gerald was very fond of gooseberries. In fact, he was so fond of them when they were nearly ripe that it was difficult for him to walk down the garden without picking one. Did I say one? I should have said several, for unless someone was looking, Gerald, I am sorry to say, would pick as many as his little hands and pockets could carry.

Now it so happened that Mother also was fond of gooseberries, to say nothing of Father, who liked to walk up and down among the bushes, trying the flavor of the different berries.

One day Daddy went down the garden for a stroll, hoping to have a fat, juicy gooseberry or two when he got down to the bushes.

But when he got there, the bushes were bare. There was not a gooseberry to be seen. Even the very big one that had been growing all by itself, and which Daddy had been watching with such pride and anticipation, had disappeared. The bushes had been stripped as completely as if a great wind had blown over them and swept all the gooseberries away.

"I wonder who could have taken all the gooseberries?"

4-3

said Daddy to himself. "It surely could not have been Gerald, for I've spoken to him so many times about picking them. Perhaps the birds have been at them again, or maybe Mamma has picked them to make some jam."

Just then a cheery voice called to him.

"Hello, Daddy! Come and look at all the things in my garden."

It was Gerald.

Daddy walked over to the little patch which he had given to the boy to cultivate.

"Look, Dad, see these lovely flowers. Aren't they beautiful?"

"They surely are," said Daddy. "Nice apples you've got, too."

"Indeed they are," said Gerald. "And I hope nobody picks them but me."

"Oh, now, aren't you a bit particular about it?" said Daddy.

"I should say I am," said Gerald. "Here I've waited all the year for them, fertilized the tree and watered it and kept the weeds from it—I should think I *am* particular about who picks my apples. If Baby touches them, I'll give him a good spanking."

34

"I see," said Daddy, his eyes wandering over the rest of Gerald's garden, and lighting on a pile of strange green objects lying partly concealed by a cabbage leaf.

Gerald, noticing the direction of Daddy's gaze, promptly put his foot on the cabbage leaf and began to talk about his sunflowers.

35

"Big sunflower that, isn't it?" he said, blushing a little.

But Daddy was not interested in sunflowers. He had become exceedingly interested in cabbages.

"Nice cabbages these," he said. "You have done well, Gerald. Do let me feel the heart of this one. You shouldn't tread on the leaves of such fine plants."

Gerald blushed more deeply as Daddy bent down to "feel" how solid the plant was.

"I didn't know that you had any gooseberry bushes in your garden," said Daddy rather sternly as he stood up again.

"I haven't," said Gerald very faintly and blushing more deeply.

"Then where did these skins come from?"

"Down the garden," said Gerald.

"I'm sorry," said Daddy. "I thought I could trust my boy. Don't you think it was very mean of you to take all those gooseberries when you knew how I have been waiting all the year for them? Haven't you seen me down there by the hour weeding them and pruning them and fertilizing them?"

Gerald seemed to recognize his own argument and looked very sorry for himself.

"It's too bad," said Daddy. "And somehow you must learn not to do it again. Seeing you have helped yourself to my gooseberries, I think I will try a few of your apples."

So Daddy began to pick the ripest of them.

"No, no, no!" cried Gerald, bursting into tears. "You mustn't pick my apples! They're mine! I've grown them all myself!"

"But what about my gooseberries?" said Daddy, proceeding to eat the fattest and rosiest apple. "If we say six gooseberries

36

equal one apple, I should think I am entitled to all the apples on this tree."

"But you mustn't pick every one of them!" cried Gerald frantically.

"I won't, on one condition."

"What's that?" asked Gerald.

"That you promise never again to take things that do not belong to you."

"All right. I'll promise," said Gerald.

"Yes," said Daddy, "and remember what the golden rule says about doing unto others as you would like them to do unto you."

Gerald tried hard to remember, and next year he picked his own apples, while Daddy had all the gooseberries he desired.

Daddy's Discovery

Ronald returned from school one day looking very sick. As he came indoors he walked across the dining room and flopped into an armchair.

"What's the matter, Ronny?" asked Mother. "You don't look very well."

"Don't feel well," said Ronald.

"What have you been eating at school?" asked Mother.

"Haven't eaten anything since dinner," said Ronny. "I just feel sick. Don't worry. I'll be better tomorrow."

"Well, supper is nearly ready."

"Don't want any supper."

"What do you want?"

"Oh, nothing. I think I'll go to bed early."

"Daddy will be back at seven; better wait till then; he likes to find you here."

"No," said Ronald, "I'm going now. Right away." So saying he went upstairs, and from the noises overhead Mother guessed that he was getting undressed right away, and in a hurry too.

38

At seven Daddy came in. "Where's Ronald?" he asked.

"In bed," said Mother.

"In bed!" repeated Daddy with surprise. "What for? I'll go up and see him."

Daddy bounded upstairs and into Ronald's room.

"What's the matter, son?" he asked.

Ronald pretended to be asleep, but Daddy knew a thing or two about that, having tried the same trick himself sometimes when he was a little boy.

"Come on now, Ronny. You're not asleep. What's the matter?"

"Feeling sick," murmured Ronny.

"Give me your hand. Let me feel your pulse."

Ronny held out his hand. Daddy felt his pulse and noticed something.

"What's this on your fingers, son?"

Ronny pulled his hand under the covers. "Nothing, Dad; paint, I think."

"Let me see your tongue."

Ronald opened his mouth. Daddy bent down very close, much closer than he really needed just to look in. Then he got up from the bed and walked over to the chair where Ronald's clothes were lying. He picked them up one by one and felt carefully in the pockets. It was rather a messy job, for some of the pockets had all sorts of treasures in them, such as bits of string, nails, dirty handkerchiefs, a half-melted caramel, an apple core, and cooky crumbs. But from the bottom of the right-hand trouser pocket Daddy hauled out a small yellow box.

He came back to Ronny, who had been lying very quiet and still during the search.

"Ronny, why do you have these matches in your pocket?"

"To light fireworks," said Ronny quietly.

"Are you sure, Ronny?" said Daddy very solemnly. "Are you really telling me the truth?"

There was a long silence.

"Tell me," said Daddy, "was that the truth?"

"No," said Ronald very, very quietly.

"I knew it wasn't," said Daddy. "As soon as I saw your hand and smelled your breath I knew you had been playing with tobacco. Am I right?"

"Yes; a boy at school dared me to try it," said Ronald, tears streaming down his cheeks.

"Oh, Ronny! I am so sorry," said Daddy. "I had hoped you would never learn that horrid, dirty, wasteful habit. I have never smoked tobacco in my life, and I wanted my son never, never to have anything to do with it."

40

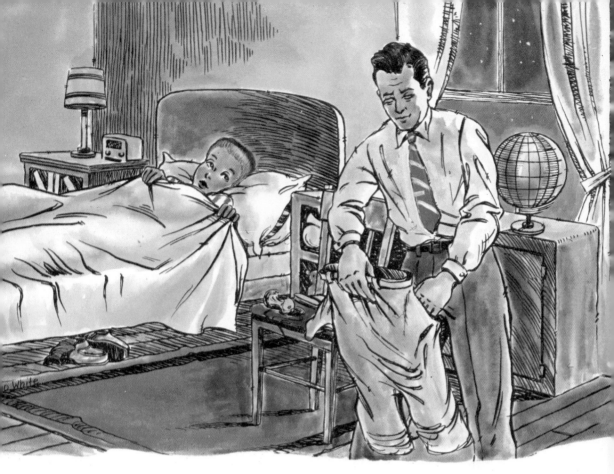

"I knew you didn't, Daddy, and I really didn't want to," said Ronny amid his tears.

"I'm sure you didn't," said Daddy. "But you must be strong next time to say No. Smoking never did anybody any good. It spoils your health, weakens your heart and lungs, stains your hands, makes your breath smell, and burns up your money."

Daddy paused, and there was a deep silence, broken only by Ronny's deep breathing and an occasional sob.

"Ronny!" said Daddy.

"Yes, Daddy."

"I want you to promise me one thing."

"Yes, Daddy."

"Give me your hand."

Ronny put it out.

"Promise me," said Daddy, taking the little hand in his, "promise me that you will never put tobacco of any kind near your mouth again."

"I promise," said Ronny.

They squeezed hands in the darkness, and the promise was sealed.

Mary's Sacrifice

Here is a delightful little story I heard some time ago. It has been told many times by a good many people, but it is so good that it will bear telling again. It is about a brave little cripple girl who lived many years ago in a poor quarter of a big city.

I don't remember her name; so I will just call her Mary.

Mary had something the matter with one of her legs so that she could not walk properly. She could only limp about, and that with difficulty. But what made matters worse was the fact that her mother also was a cripple, and suffered in the same way. Worse still, her father was a lazy and cruel man, spending most of his time in saloons, and often coming home quite drunk.

Some kind people heard about poor little Mary, and made arrangements for her to be taken to a beautiful home, where she would receive every care and where her leg might be made better. Everything was planned for Mary to go, and the kind people came to get her.

But to their great surprise Mary refused to go. They urged

her and coaxed her, telling her what a lovely place it was to which they were going to take her, and picturing the glory of the open country, the fields and flowers and trees. Even Mary's mamma joined in, trying to persuade her to go, for she knew how much good it would do her to get away from the crowded city.

But still Mary refused.

"I can't go, I can't go," she said firmly, though there were big tears in her eyes.

"Why not?" asked the kind people.

"Because——" and Mary hesitated while tears rolled down her cheeks.

44

"Go on, do tell us," coaxed the kind people.

"Because," said Mary, "because Father stays out late and drinks, and when he comes home drunk and starts beating Mamma, I get *in between*."

Whether Mary ever went to the beautiful home the kind people had planned for her I do not know, but the simple story of her courage and self-sacrifice will live forever. She was willing to give up the greatest opportunity that life had offered her—to turn her back on the fields and the flowers and the great open spaces that called to her so strongly—just to stand by her mamma and save her from harm. She was ready to sacrifice all just to do what seemed her duty, to get "in between," to take the hard knocks, and to keep her mamma safe.

"In between!" What a beautiful thought! Say, children, would you be willing to do the same for your mamma? Would you sacrifice so much?

Of course you could not do the same as little Mary, for your daddy, I am sure, is not like hers; but could you not get in between Mamma and overwork, between Mamma and over-worry? Could you not, at a sacrifice sometimes, get in between her and washing the dishes or minding the baby or setting the table or washing the floor or cleaning the steps? Could you not, by giving up a little play, help her much by getting in between her and ever so many of the little cares of life?

"In between!" Would you not like to be the little peace-maker both at home and at school, getting in between when others fight, taking hard knocks at times, but saving the weak from harm?

There are so many beautiful ways in which you can get "in between." Just as Jesus came in between us and sin, so you

45

can always try to do the same when other children are saying or doing wrong things. You can get in between with something that is pure and lovely until they also think more beautiful thoughts.

And there are the poor. You can, by a little sacrifice, get in between them and their poverty.

There are so many people who are sad. By sympathy and kindly words and deeds you can get in between them and their sorrow.

How much there is for each one of us to do! How many ways there are for us to do as Mary did, to show her noble and beautiful spirit, and to get "in between."

The Stowaway

Some years ago a small steamer ran into a terrific storm in the South Atlantic Ocean. For three days the ship was tossed and buffeted by the mighty waves. One mast was carried away, and the steering gear was damaged.

Toward the close of the third day the storm increased in severity. The sky became blacker than ever, and the poor sailors realized that worse times were ahead. Suddenly, amid the crash

47

of thunder, the cry was raised that the ship had sprung a leak.

In a moment the pumps were manned, but soon it was discovered that the water was rising in the hold faster than the men could pump it out. They worked desperately for another hour, but all in vain. Seeing that the task was hopeless and that the ship was doomed, the captain ordered that the boats be lowered.

To the dismay of all, it was found that there was but one of the boats that remained undamaged by the waves—the rest were so battered that they would never stay afloat in such a sea. There was nothing to do but cram the entire crew into the one boat.

Quickly the men climbed in, filling the boat to its utmost capacity. There was just room enough to squeeze in the captain, who had bravely remained behind till the last.

He was about to step over the side of the ship to climb down to the boat, when, hearing a cry, he looked around. There, running toward him across the deck, was a strange young lad, dirty-faced and clothed in rags. He was a stowaway.

Where the lad had hidden himself or how he had kept alive since the ship left port, the captain did not know, and there was no time to ask.

"Quick, lad!" he shouted, stepping back onto the ship. "Down the rope!"

The lad needed no second invitation. In a moment he was over the side and climbing down the rope into the boat—filling the last available space.

"Come on!" shouted the men to the captain, willing to overload the boat rather than leave him behind to perish.

"Push off!" yelled the captain, above the howling of the storm. He knew full well that one more in the boat would certainly capsize it and perhaps cause the death of all.

So the men pushed off, and not a moment too soon. Hardly were they at a safe distance from the ship when it turned on its side and plunged into the sea, bearing the noble captain to his ocean grave.

After many days of hardship the men in the boat were picked up by a passing vessel and finally reached home again. Never did the stowaway forget the captain's self-sacrifice. The memory of that heroic deed changed his life. He felt he must be worthy of so priceless a gift. In his pocket he carried the captain's photograph, to which he would point as he told and retold the thrilling story, saying, "He gave his life for me."

This story helps us to understand what Jesus has done for each one of us. He is the Captain; we are the stowaways. We do not in the least deserve to be saved and have a place in His beautiful home. But Jesus died to make this possible; and although it was many years ago that He made His wonderful sacrifice for us, it is available for every boy and girl today. As the stowaway afterward talked about the captain, so we, too, should be glad to tell others of all that Jesus has done for us. We, too, can say, "He died for me."

50

Weighed in the Balances

Of all the wonderful things to be seen in London, there is nothing, perhaps, more marvelous than the balances at the royal mint.

There is one balance there so delicately adjusted that if you were to take two pieces of paper and place one in each of the scale pans, then write your signature on one piece, the weight of your signature would be indicated!

It is of the utmost importance, of course, that these balances be absolutely accurate, because the whole money system of the country depends on them.

You see, banks do not *count* money; they *weigh* it. Consequently every individual piece of money must weigh exactly the same as every other piece. Otherwise some people would get many more coins than other people for the same value in paper money, and much trouble would result.

There is another reason why these balances have to be perfect. As the precious metal passes on its way from the melting pots, through all the various processes until it becomes "coin of the realm," it is highly important that none should be-

come lost. As you can imagine, much might be lost in one way or another if every care were not taken.

So what do they do? They weigh the metal from room to room. The same amount of metal that comes into a department must be checked out of it. So again very delicate balances are needed, for the tiniest difference means a lot when you're weighing gold or silver.

But it is when the coins are almost at the end of their journey that the most astonishing feats are performed by the balances.

Though the coins have been weighed already several times on their way, they are given a final test on scales that are so finely adjusted that they will automatically separate coins into three classes —"correct," "light," and "heavy." It is almost uncanny to watch these scales at work, with the different pieces of money falling with unfailing accuracy into their proper places.

You simply can't deceive these balances. Put in a coin that is one-thousandth part of an ounce too light, and it will be thrown out. Put in one that is a tiny fraction too heavy and out it goes. Every one *must* be perfect.

As I looked at all these balances I couldn't help thinking of the wonderful lesson the workmen in the mint are being taught all the time, though I suppose they are all too busy to think about it. But there before them, in every room, is a constant reminder that their work is being carefully watched and checked to a thousandth part of an ounce.

If all the work you do at school, or helping Father in the garden or Mother in the kitchen, were examined with equal thoroughness, what result would be seen? How much would deserve to be "thrown out" as imperfect? More than you would like to admit, I suspect.

There is something else of which these balances remind me. Do you remember a text which says, "Every idle word that men shall speak, they shall give account thereof in the day of judgment"? Matthew 12:36.

That suggests, doesn't it, that even though we do not "weigh our words," Somebody else is doing so? The heavenly balances, adjusted even more finely than those at the mint, indicate with alarming precision the weight of every word we utter. And some of the things we say, I'm afraid, don't weigh very much in the sight of God.

How careful this thought should make us, in all our words and actions!

In the book of Daniel is the story of a king who scoffed at God and boasted vainly of his own deeds. Suddenly, in the midst of a great feast, there were seen on the wall of his

palace the fingers of a man's hand—writing in letters of fire.

You remember what was written?

"Thou art weighed in the balances, and art found wanting." Daniel 5:27.

The angels had been listening to the king's proud speech. His foolish words had been weighed in the heavenly balances, and found light as air. In fact, his whole life was shown to be vain and worthless, full of wasted opportunities for good. So the decree of doom went forth from the heavenly watchers, and that night Belshazzar was slain.

One day, and no one knows how soon, we, too, shall be "weighed in the balances." What will the record reveal? Shall we be found wanting?

PAINTING BY JOHN GOURLEY

Doggie Love

We all love dogs, don't we? Nice dogs, I mean. I suspect you have been looking at those two lovely little puppies in the picture and wishing and wishing that they would suddenly become real and jump into your arms.

I wish they would, for I know they would make you very happy.

Dogs can be so friendly and lovable. Of course, like most boys and girls, they get into all sorts of mischief, but you can't help loving them just the same.

Treated properly, they often become the most loyal of friends. Sometimes, too, they will not only remain faithful to their human masters but also be true to their doggie chums.

Which brings me to a very sad story. So get out your hand-kerchiefs. You may need them.

Some years ago there lived in Liverpool, England, a dog called Chubby and another known as Old Bob. They were the best of friends, eating together, playing together, and getting into mischief together. If you saw Old Bob alone you could be sure Chubby was not far away. They enjoyed each other's company like twin brothers.

And then, alas, came a very sad day. Poor Chubby became ill and died. Old Bob couldn't understand what had happened to him. All he knew was that there was no Chubby for him to play with. He looked for him everywhere but could not find him. He called to him in his own doggie language, but there was no answer.

Then he was taken out to the Liverpool Dog Cemetery, where poor Chubby had been buried. There was no Chubby for Old Bob to see, but somehow he understood. Next day he visited the grave by himself. The day after he went there again. He could not keep away from the place. And every day for three years Old Bob went to that tomb to mourn for his doggie friend. For all I know he is going there still, keeping his daily watch by Chubby's resting place.

I wonder what he thinks about when he's there, and whether he has still a little hope that one day, perhaps, he will run into Chubby again round the corner.

Poor Old Bob!

Did you ever hear of such faithful doggie love as this?

A True Dog Story

Some remarkable stories have been told about dogs, some of them, indeed, so strange that one wonders if they can really be true. Here is one, however, that actually happened.

Some years ago, in company with some friends, I visited a large house on a big country estate. The house had a large and beautiful yard in front of it. One gate in this yard led to the farm buildings, and another opened onto the main driveway.

The lady of the house, showing us around her estate, presently took us through the gate leading to the farm buildings. Immediately, from every direction, great dogs rushed upon us. They were very much bigger than the beautiful family dogs in our picture, and more like huge bloodhounds. I had never seen so many big dogs swarming around me before. I began to think it would be as well to get back to the other side of the gate as quickly as possible.

Then an amazing thing happened. I could hardly believe my eyes. The lady lifted her right hand and spoke just one word.

59

This family of beautiful white dogs beg for their daily treat from their mistress.

"Obedience!" she cried with a note of command.

Instantly the dogs stopped frisking about us, and followed their mistress like a flock of lambs.

The lady told us that some of these big dogs were, in fact, only puppies six months old, but that all of them were being trained with the utmost care to obey instantly her word of command.

A little later we observed the most striking example of this perfect obedience that I have ever seen.

We returned to the front yard through the other gate that led onto the main driveway. The dogs had accompanied us all around the farm, and as we entered the front yard we fully expected them to follow us. But they did not.

Believe it or not as you please, those great big dogs lined up in a row across the open gateway and

60

would not so much as put a paw into the front yard! And, mind you, there was no gate or obstruction of any kind to keep them back, not even a painted mark on the ground.

I looked at the dogs in sheer amazement. They stood there like so many soldiers on guard. Then one of them took a pace forward.

Instantly a voice behind me called out the magic word, "Obedience!"

Without a moment's hesitation the offending dog went back to his place in the line!

And then another remarkable thing happened. A little terrier, the house dog, suddenly appeared on the scene. He came bounding into the yard, making himself quite at home. I turned in surprise to the lady.

"Oh, it's quite all right," she replied with a smile. "He is the only dog allowed in the front yard. The others know they must stay outside."

"Well!" I said, "if that isn't extraordinary!"

And the last thing I remember about that visit is the picture of that row of giant dogs lined up like a regiment of soldiers across the open gateway.

As I came away I began to think what a happy world it would be if all the children in it were just half as obedient as those dogs! What a blessing it would be if when parents said, "Obedience!" the children would instantly do what they were told without a fuss.

How is it in your home? Do you always obey pleasantly, happily, without a murmur?

Not always? Well, then, I want you to read this text in the third verse of the first chapter of Isaiah:

"The ox knoweth his owner, and the ass his master's crib: but Israel doth not know, My people doth not consider."

This means that, in God's sight, the animals are oftentimes more thoughtful and considerate than human beings. They remember who feeds them, but children sometimes do not. The animals try to serve faithfully those who look after them, but children sometimes treat Father and Mother with much rudeness and disrespect. What must God think of us when we act like that?

We mustn't let it be said that the animals are better than we, surely! Of course not! So next time Mother says, "Obedience!" I want you to think of those wonderful dogs I have told you about, and, mind, you mustn't put even a paw across the line!

Rosalind's Medicine

People who live in hot countries have to take great care of their health. If they don't, they usually catch some serious disease, which causes them much pain and discomfort, and sometimes death.

One of these diseases is malaria. Even the most careful people sometimes get it, but it has been found that if one takes a medicine called quinine, the attacks are much less severe.

Now, quinine is not a very nice medicine. It has a rather bitter taste, and most children have a strong dislike for it.

Anyhow, Rosalind certainly had. She hated it, and did not hesitate to tell her mother so.

She lived on a mission station in Africa, and malaria was

very prevalent in the district. The whole family suffered from it a good deal, Rosalind included.

One day she felt another attack coming on. Mother noticed it, put her to bed, and went for the quinine.

But Rosalind did not want the quinine. She disliked it so much she thought she would rather have the malaria than take the horrid stuff.

Mother begged and implored her to take it, but in vain. You know the scene that so often takes place when a little girl is asked to take some nasty medicine! Well, that is just what happened then. Rosalind was obstinate. She would not take quinine. Mother, knowing that the little girl's life depended on her taking the medicine, became more insistent.

"You must take it, Rosalind," she said.

"I don't want to," said the little girl stubbornly.

"But you will be very ill indeed, if you do not take it," said Mother.

"Then I'll be ill," said Rosalind defiantly.

"Well," said Mother sternly, "you must take it. I do not want you to be ill. There is too much to do here already without having a sick child to care for."

"I'll tell you what," said Rosalind, "if you will leave the medicine on the table and go out of the room, I promise you it will be all gone when you come back."

"All right," said Mother happily, glad for some way out of the struggle. "There it is now. Drink it all up, there's a good girl, and when I come back I will bring you something nice."

Mother went out and closed the door. A little later she re-

turned to the room, saw the glass was empty, and handed Rosalind a piece of candy. She thought Rosalind did not look very happy, but put it down to the nasty taste of the medicine.

That night Rosalind's temperature went up ever so high, and she became delirious.

Mother grew alarmed. Poor Rosalind became steadily worse. Very sick, and racked with pain, she almost wished she could die.

Every moment she could spare, Mother sat by the little girl's bedside to soothe and comfort her.

"Mother," said Rosalind the next evening, "there's something I've got to tell you."

"Is there?" said Mother. "I wonder what it is. But there, perhaps you had better not talk much now. When you get better you can tell me."

"No, I must tell you in case—in case—I don't get better," said Rosalind.

"Whatever can it be then?" asked Mother.

"Well, Mother dear," said Rosalind, "I know why I am so ill."

"Do you, dear?"

"Yes, Mother. You know that medicine I refused to take yesterday?"

"Yes, I remember," said Mother with a smile. "You mean the medicine you wouldn't take till I went out of the room?"

"Yes," said Rosalind very sadly and talking with difficulty. "I never took it."

"Rosalind!" Mother's voice was sharp.

"Yes, I threw it out the window."

There was silence for several minutes.

66

"Are you very cross, Mother?" asked Rosalind after a little while.

"Not cross, only sorry," said Mother.

"Oh, that's much worse," said Rosalind.

"But you understand now, dear, don't you?" said Mother.

"I do indeed."

"It costs too much, doesn't it, dear, to disobey?"

"It does," said Rosalind.

They squeezed hands in the gathering darkness while Rosalind resolved that if Jesus would make her well, she would try never to deceive her mother again.

Finding Things

Isn't it annoying to lose something that you value very much? I should say it is!

If only there were some way of finding lost things, wouldn't that be useful? Then we'd never have to worry about them any more.

Well, there is a way. I wouldn't want to say that it always works, for there are some things that are better lost than found, but it does work sometimes, and you ought to know about it.

I lost something the other day that simply had to be found.

Where was it? What could have happened to it? I could not tell. That I had had it in my hand some days before I was certain, but now, just when it was most needed, it was nowhere to be found.

I turned out every drawer and cupboard. I hunted high and low. I asked everybody who might have seen it. But all to no avail. No one had seen it. The precious piece of paper had completely disappeared.

What made it worse was the fact that I was dreadfully rushed at the time, with a thousand and one things demanding

68

attention. There simply wasn't time to go on looking over and over again.

Yet it had to be found. And now——

Well, I'll tell you.

I shut my eyes just for a moment, and said, "Dear Lord, You know how very busy I am, and how I must find that document right away. Please find it for me."

I opened my eyes, and believe it or not, there it was, less than three feet from my nose!

Perhaps you will say, "Of course it had been there all the time."

Maybe it had, but for some reason I had not been able to

see it. Perhaps Jesus wanted me to think about Him just then. Anyway, I did, and it worked!

Which reminds me that a young lady spoke to me the other day and told me how, on going home from college one day, she lost her purse with a dollar and a half in it. That was a lot of money for her to lose, as she was poor. She felt she must have it back, so she told Jesus about it and asked His help.

Three weeks passed, three weeks of waiting and wondering. Then one morning a package arrived through the mail containing the lost purse, with the dollar and a half inside! Very remarkable, you must admit.

But here's another story. Not many months ago there was a knock at my door, and a very worried woman told me that while in London that day she had lost her keys—house keys, trunk keys, and all the rest.

"Where did you lose them?" I inquired.

"At the zoo," she replied.

"The zoo!" I exclaimed. "What a place to lose anything!"

She agreed, especially as that day the place had been crowded with thousands and thousands of visitors.

There was nothing to do but pray. Absolutely no other hope. And how she prayed, bless her dear old heart! Heaven couldn't help but answer such a prayer of faith as that.

Days passed. She had to get a carpenter or a locksmith or somebody to let her into her home, but still she believed the keys would come back.

One afternoon a car drew up at her door and a well-dressed man stepped out.

"Excuse me," he said, "did you happen to lose something in the zoo several days ago?"

"Yes," she cried eagerly, her heart beating fast with excitement, "my keys!"

"It gives me pleasure to return them to you," said the gentleman. "I found them there, and saw your name and address on the tag."

He had driven twenty miles to deliver them!

Perhaps it was only an accident, a happen-so, but I do not think so. Jesus has His own wonderful way of answering the prayers of His loving children, and He delights to help them in every time of need.

In other words, Jesus doesn't want us to worry, but rather

71

to tell Him all about our troubles. If you have lost something and feel that it is important that you should have it again, say a little prayer and see what happens.

One thing is sure. He knows where it is, for He knows everything. And if it is for your good and for the glory of God that you should have it again, He will surely help you find it.

It's worth trying, anyway, isn't it?

72

The Storm

Ken should have been a very happy boy. Was he not at the seaside for a glorious two weeks' vacation? Did he not have a new bucket and spade? Had not Daddy given him a new boat with red sails? Did he not have beautiful sands to play on, and the cool, refreshing sea in which to bathe?

He did, but he was not happy.

He had just had a very good dinner, too, but still he was not happy. In fact, he was feeling very rebellious, and he looked it. An ugly scowl covered his face, and his lips pouted out quite half an inch.

Of course it was all about nothing, as usual. Daddy had asked him to stop throwing stones, because it was annoying people on the beach. Ken thought he should be allowed to throw stones as he wished, and Daddy had had to say "Stop!" with a lot of meaning in it. Hence that terrible look on Ken's face.

"Come and help build a big sand castle," said Daddy, trying to make things easy for him. "The tide will soon be up, and we can watch it attack our fortress." He reached for Ken's hand.

"Don't want to build any old castle," said Ken.

"Come along, come along," said Daddy.

"Don't want to," said Ken fiercely, turning around and walking away.

"All right," said Daddy, "I'll build it myself." And so saying he picked up a spade and began to dig.

Meanwhile Ken trudged on and on along the beach. Really it was a very funny sight, for he was only a little boy of nine, and there he was with his hands deep in his pockets and his brow all puckered up as if he were plotting a revolution. Farther and farther he wandered. He did not seem to notice the passing of time or the fact that he had left his family and friends far behind.

Still boiling with anger, he trudged savagely on. He didn't want to be with anybody, he told himself. He didn't want to play with the others any more. He wanted to be by himself and do just as he pleased. Now he could throw stones where he liked and when he liked, for there wasn't anybody anywhere. And he was glad, glad, glad about it, that he was!

Just then a sudden chilling of the air made him look upward. Till now the sun had been shining brightly. The past few days, indeed, had all been fine and hot. But now a dark cloud obscured the sun, and a cold gust of wind came from the southwest.

Ken slowed down a little. He did not like the look of the sky. But, turn back? No, indeed, he wouldn't. He kept trudging along.

Ten minutes later Ken looked at the sky again. Almost all the blue had gone. Rising fast from the horizon were black, angry-looking clouds. The occasional gusts of wind had become a gale. The sea that had been so calm a little while before was being lashed to fury.

A dull boom in the distance brought Ken to a standstill. His little face lost its scowl and turned very pale. He didn't like storms.

Boom! Boom! Boom! rolled the thunder, getting louder and louder.

Flash! Across the black clouds leaped lightning more terrible than any Ken had ever seen before.

Crack! Boom! Crash! A terrific peal of thunder sounded right above him.

Ken stood still, petrified with fright. Wildly he looked around for shelter, but there was none. Along that lonely beach not even a sea gull could have found cover.

And now the rain!

Swish! Swish! Swish! Driven hard by the gale, it beat upon the beach and splashed with an uncanny hissing into the sea.

Poor Ken was soaked in a moment. Water streamed through his shirt. He dropped beside a breakwater and buried his head in his hands.

Boom! Boom! rolled the thunder, as loud and terrible as before.

"Oh dear!" cried Ken to himself, "why did I come so far away? I wish I had stayed with the others. Oh dear! Will this thunder never stop?"

Crash! Another terrifying peal thundered over his head. It was too much for the little chap. Tears flowed at last, rolling down his cheeks and mingling with the rain that was pouring in torrents over him.

Ah, what was that? Another sound had reached his ears amid the storm. Surely that was a footstep. Someone was walking on the beach somewhere. How welcome was the sound!

Ken looked up and peered over the breakwater through the blinding rain.

Hurrah! Yes! Someone with an umbrella held close and low before him as he fought his way against the gale.

Ken felt he had never been so glad to see anybody before. He called out, but his little voice was drowned by the storm.

Crack! A flash and a report right overhead again sent Ken huddling beside the breakwater.

But the footsteps drew nearer. Ken peeped over again. Yes, there was the umbrella, much nearer now.

Then another fear gripped his heart. Would this person care for him? Would he want to stop in this storm? Would he want to share his umbrella in such rain as this? Ken huddled down again in fear and discouragement. Oh, why had he come so far alone?

The footsteps stopped. Ken looked up. The umbrella was overhead.

"Hello, Ken," said a familiar voice, "what on earth are you doing here?"

"Oh, Dad! Did *you* come for me?" cried Ken, tears breaking out afresh as he threw his arms around Daddy. "Oh, I'm so glad you've come! I'm sorry I was so mean. I won't be naughty any more."

"That's all right, son," said Daddy. "We'll forget that. But if you ever want to go walking on your own again, I hope you won't choose a day like this."

And then, with the gale behind them and the thunder gradually rolling away into the distance, they walked back hand in hand together.

"Better to Die"

There is a very interesting story told of the Rev. C. P. Golightly, a Church of England minister who died many years ago.

He was a very good man and a fine preacher, but he is chiefly remembered because of his profound hatred of falsehood. He could not tolerate anything that was not absolutely straightforward and truthful.

A great lover of children, he often taught in the village schools around Oxford and made it his special concern to impress upon the boys and girls the importance of always speaking the truth.

At every school to which he went he made the children learn by heart this little rhyme:

> "Better to die
> Than tell a lie."

Then whenever he passed through the village again at some later time, he would say to the friends who went with him, "I will tell you which of these are my children; just listen."

79

Then he would go up to one of the boys, and chucking him under the chin, would say, "Better to die——" and if the boy replied, "Than tell a lie," he would turn to his friends and say, "You see, that's one of my children."

He never failed to recognize any of his children by this very simple method, and the boys and girls, knowing that they might meet him at any time, saw to it that they did not forget what he had taught them.

And now I wonder—supposing I should meet you somewhere this evening and say what that old minister said to his children, what would you reply? If I were to say to you, "Better to die——" would you say, without a moment's hesitation, "Than tell a lie"?

Would you—every one of you?

I know you would, if you really believed it, as I sincerely hope you do.

There have been men and women in the past who have actually died rather than tell a lie, preferring fearful tortures and a cruel death to life stained with falsehood. No nobler souls have ever lived. The world needs more such men and women today.

Would you be one of them? Then remember Golightly's words.

Who knows how many hundreds of boys and girls were saved by them from lives of falsehood? Like warning bells they rang in their ears again and again, as temptations came to them and the great enemy sought to lead them into sin.

Let these same splendid words ring in yours.

Susie's Suitcase

Daddy was at the wheel and Susie was sitting beside him. Mamma was on the back seat with the two boys. All of a sudden there was a shout.

"Look out, Daddy!" cried Susie. "There's a suitcase on the road."

Daddy had seen it already and, putting on the brakes, brought the car to a stop just in time to avoid running over it. Susie was out first, with the boys right behind her. Here was a great find and they all wanted to look inside at once. Who could guess what valuable things might be in it!

Snap, snap went the fasteners, and suddenly there was another shout from Susie.

"Oh, Mamma, look! Come and see! It's full of baby clothes —beautiful dresses, just the right size for my baby doll. Oh, how wonderful!"

"Somebody must be feeling very sad about losing all these lovely things," said Mamma. "I wonder how we can find out who owns them?"

"But aren't we going to keep them?" asked Susie. "Why, Mamma, these dresses and panties and things are just what I have been wanting. My dolly will look wonderful in them."

"But, darling, we couldn't do that," said Mamma. "These things belong to somebody else. To keep them would be stealing, wouldn't it?"

They put the suitcase in the car and drove home. Once there they opened it again and searched hard for the owner's name. At last they found it, sewed onto one of the garments. Mother looked up the name in the telephone directory, and there it was. Then she put through a call. How happy the lady was to know that her suitcase had been found by such honest

people! By and by she called for it, and insisted on paying a small reward.

"It's too bad," said Susie, when the woman had gone. "I hoped we wouldn't find out who owned it."

"But, darling," said Mamma, "isn't it much better this way? If you had kept all those nice things, you would never have enjoyed them; for you would always have felt that they belonged to somebody else; and now we have made another friend."

"Maybe so," said Susie, "but I wish I had those baby clothes for my dolly just the same."

Now it so happened—mind you, it really *did* happen— that just one week later Mamma, Daddy, Susie, and her two brothers left home on a long trip. With so many in the car, they tied some of the baggage on the top of the car. Early one morning, in high spirits, they set off for their destination. For several hours they continued on their way and then Daddy said he thought it was time for lunch and a rest. So they all got out and sat down to eat by the roadside.

All of a sudden somebody noticed that the rope that had been tied around the baggage was loose.

"One of the suitcases is missing!" cried Daddy.

Alas, it was only too true.

"Whose suitcase was it?" asked Mamma.

"Susie's," said Daddy. "I'm sure it was."

"Mine!" cried Susie. "Why, it had all my dresses in it and things and—oh, it's just terrible! Are you sure it was mine that got lost?"

"Quite sure," said Daddy. "It's too bad, but there's really nothing we can do about it. I'm afraid it's gone for good."

Then Mamma spoke up. Something had flashed across her mind.

"Why," she said, "how strange that we should find a suitcase just a week ago and then lose one of our own today! Maybe, since we did the right thing about the other suitcase, God will help us find this one."

"Do you think so?" said Susie.

"I surely do," said Mamma. "Let us tell Him all about it now before we go on."

And they did. There by the side of the road, in a beautiful little prayer, Mamma told God the whole story of the two suitcases, asking Him to help them find the one that was missing.

After that Daddy drove back along the highway five miles or so, but there was no sign of the case. Then he drove on to

85

the next town and put an advertisement in the local paper. After that they continued on their way, wondering whether they ever would hear of the suitcase again.

One day passed—two—three. Still no word reached them. Susie was still wearing the same dress in which she started out on the journey.

Then, believe it or not, a telegram arrived. "Suitcase found," it said.

Was Susie happy? I should say she was. And thankful, too —not only to God but to the honest soul who had found *her* things and given them back to her.

From that day on she saw new meaning in the words, "All things whatsoever ye would that men should do to you, do ye even so to them." Matthew 7:12.

How Toby Made Peace

Now look here, children," said Daddy, bundling Paul and Barbara out of the living room into the garden. "I simply can't stand it any longer. You stay outside until you can learn to stop grumbling and be more polite."

And with that Daddy went back into the living room, sat down in his easy chair, put his feet up on the fireguard, and went to sleep.

Paul and Barbara knew they deserved their fate, and soon began to feel sorry that their behavior had annoyed their dear daddy so much.

For a little while they did not know what to do, and wandered aimlessly up and down the garden path in silence.

"Ah, here's Toby coming!" cried Paul. "Toby, Toby, Toby! Good old Toby, where have you been?"

Toby wagged his tail, as if to assure them that he had been a very good dog all the time he had been missing.

"And you haven't been chasing any cats?" asked Barbara. Toby merely yawned, then wagged his tail again, as if to say that he wouldn't think of doing any such thing, although, if the truth must be told, there was nothing that so stirred Toby's wrath as the sight of a pussy's whiskers.

"I've got an idea," said Paul.

"Tell me," said Barbara.

"Let's give Toby a bath; he hasn't had one for a long time and he's getting quite dirty again."

"I think that would be fun," said Barbara. "It's better than doing nothing. You get the tub out of the shed, and I'll slip into the kitchen quietly and get a towel and some soap."

"Right!" cried Paul. "And won't that be nice, Toby? Toby have a bath? Dear old Toby!"

Again Toby wagged his tail, though it was not quite so happy a wag as before. He was not fond of being bathed, and sometimes objected to it very strongly. He looked very suspiciously at the tub as Paul brought it out of the shed, and decided it was time to take a short walk down the garden.

Barbara soon returned, bringing a towel and a kettle of warm water.

"Where's Toby?" she asked.

"Ran off," said Paul. "We shall have to catch him."

"Toby, Toby!" called Barbara.

But Toby was a wise old dog and guessed why he was wanted. He walked a little farther on. Paul and Barbara followed him, and after an exciting chase caught him in a corner by the greenhouse.

"Bad Toby! Bad Toby!" said Paul as he dragged him by the collar up toward the shed. "Toby mustn't run away from us any more. Toby's going to have a nice bath."

Toby didn't appreciate the last remark at all. His tail had stopped wagging and his eyes had a strange, determined look.

88

It was quite a job to get him into the bath. Paul lifted his front legs and Barbara his back legs, and together they got him in. But it was quite another matter to keep him in. For a moment or two he stood quite still while Paul sponged his ears. Then all of a sudden he began to kick and jump and splash water all over.

"Hold him, Paul," cried Barbara, "or he'll jump out of the tub!"

"Can't you see I'm holding him as hard as I can?" said Paul. "You go on washing him."

Barbara started, while Paul tried his best to keep Toby in the bath. She got as far as covering the whole of him with a good lather of soap, when suddenly something happened.

For a moment Toby became very still. He seemed to forget that he was being bathed. His eyes had caught sight of some-

thing down in the garden. His back stiffened, his tail stood up, and with a loud "Yap, yap," he shook his collar free, leaped from the bath, and dashed away at top speed.

"Stop him!" cried Barbara helplessly, wiping the water from her dress and ankles.

"You'll never stop him!" said Paul. "Can't you see there's Mrs. Tompkins' cat!"

"Oh dear!" cried Barbara. "I do hope he doesn't hurt her."

There was no fear of that, for this particular pussy had often been chased by Toby, and knew every possible hiding place in both the garden and the house.

"Oh, look!" cried Barbara, as dog and cat raced hither and yon, across the flower beds, in and out among the trees and bushes. "What a dreadful mess Toby will be!"

She was right. By this time Toby's soap-covered body had gathered up mud, leaves, and bits of twigs, until he looked as if he had never had a bath in his life.

"I only hope Daddy doesn't look out the window until we've got the little rascal cleaned up," said Paul.

"You're right," said Barbara.

But there was no need for them to worry about Daddy; he was still sleeping soundly, quite unconscious of what was going on outside.

"Now you can catch

him," said Barbara as pussy did a sudden turn and came rushing up the garden toward them, Toby close behind. "Grab him as he goes by."

But it was easier said than done. Paul made a grab, but his hand rested upon a greasy mixture of soap and mud, and away went Toby faster than ever.

"Look!" cried Barbara. "Look where the cat's going."

They might well look. Growing tired, and seeking a place of safety, pussy had spied the half-open window of the living room.

With a mighty spring she leaped onto the window sill, dropped down inside, and dived under an armchair that was drawn up near the fireplace.

Paul and Barbara held their breath. Would Toby follow? Could he possibly jump so high?

"Toby! Toby!" they both shrieked, hoping to call him away.

It was in vain. With a jump such as he had never made before, Toby got his paws upon the window sill and scrambled over. He was in the living room. Dirty, muddy, soapy Toby was in the living room!

All that happened next had better not be printed. Suffice it to say that Toby, forgetting the object of his chase in the presence of his master, jumped up in his usual friendly way upon the sleeping form in the armchair. Waking with a start, Daddy found his hands clasping a strange, warm, wriggling, soapy mass upon his knees.

91

"What *shall* we do?" said Paul. "Daddy will be awfully cross with us."

"There's only one thing to do," said Barbara. "We had better go in right now and say we're sorry."

"All right," said Paul. "I'll come with you."

And away they went. As they reached the living room, the French doors opened and out came Toby, a little more quickly even than he had gone in. Daddy stood inside. He looked very stern. As for his clothes, they were a terrible sight. Just covered with soapy dirt!

"We are dreadfully sorry," said Barbara. "We never dreamed he would do it, and we'll clean up all the mess and brush your trousers and everything. Do please forgive us."

Daddy looked at the two children and then down at his clothes. Then his face broke into the least bit of a smile.

"Oh, you two terrible children!" he said. "But I suppose I shall have to forgive you once again."

And Paul and Barbara put their arms around his neck and hugged him "ever so tight."

New Hearts for Old

Have I ever told you the story of a radio set I bought some years ago? No? Then you *will* be interested. Just listen.

You see, I had wanted a really good radio ever so badly for quite a long time, for I can't stand those cheap sets that distort the sounds and make people talk and sing with squeaky, rasping voices.

Well, the months and years passed by, and still I did not see the radio that I had pictured in my mind. My friends all bought new ones and wondered why I didn't do the same; but I always answered their questions by saying, "When I see the right radio, I'll buy it, but not till then."

Then one day it was whispered to me that a gentleman who owned one of the finest radios ever made was leaving the country and was selling out his home. I went to see him, and there, in his drawing room, I saw what I had been seeking for a long time.

So far as I was concerned, it was love at first sight. Or rather, at first sound. For when he turned it on, I sat enraptured with its beautiful tone. I knew at once it was the radio of my dreams.

To cut a long story short, we finally agreed on the price, so low that I could hardly believe my good fortune, and the radio became mine.

Two days later a truck drew up at my house and two men staggered in with the beautiful new piece of furniture and placed it carefully in the corner of my dining room.

As soon as they were gone I stood for some time looking at the radio with great joy and, I am afraid, more than a little human pride.

I never thought I would own anything so lovely. I plugged it into the wall socket.

So far as I could see, all was ready and I began to turn the various knobs on the set.

And then, oh, tragedy!

There were grunts and squeaks and groans and roars and rattles, but no music. Try as I would, I could get nothing out of that beautiful radio but the same terrible confusion of sound.

Again and again I moved the little knobs this way and that, turning the current on and off, trying one thing after another, but all with the same result. I could get absolutely nothing out of it but the same dreadful groans and shrieks, as if it were full of evil spirits.

I was in despair. What could I do?

At last I telephoned a friend who understands radio, and asked him to come over at once and help me.

He came, and wasn't I glad to see him!

But the same thing happened to him. As he turned the knobs, the set roared and rattled as before, and I felt sure that if his skilled hands could do no better than mine, there was indeed no hope.

Then he asked if he might open the back of the set and look inside.

I told him he could do anything he liked if only he would get good music out of it.

Several minutes passed, while my friend knelt on the floor with his head buried inside the set.

"Say," he said, after a while, "how about your tubes?"

"I don't know," I replied. "What do you think?"

"Well," he said, "personally I think they are either worn out or have been jarred on the journey."

"Then if that's the trouble," I said, "get some new ones, and get them as quickly as you can."

He was a good fellow and dashed off at once. Before long he was back again, bringing the new tubes.

I shall never forget the next few minutes. He took the old tubes out and put the new tubes in. Then he switched on the electric current again, turned the knobs ever so carefully, and——

Ah! all was different now. Out from the set came the most glorious music I had ever heard, distant and unearthly at first, but swelling into loud, majestic tones that fairly shook the house.

My dream had come true, although before it was possible I had had to change the tubes.

And do you know, children, whenever I think of that experience, my mind goes to that text in Ezekiel in which God says, "A new heart also will I give you, and a new spirit will I put within you: and I will take away the stony heart out of your flesh, and I will give you an heart of flesh." Ezekiel 36:26.

It seems to me that we are all very much like that radio

96

of mine. As long as we have old tubes inside, or, in other words, as long as our hearts are stony, so long it will be impossible to get any good music out of us. Stony hearts produce nothing but grumbling and growling; naughty words and sullen mutterings; and everything that is unkind and unholy.

If you hear a boy being disrespectful to his father, or cross with his brother, or rude to his mother, you may know that he has old tubes inside and needs to have them changed.

Or if you hear a girl finding fault with her food, or her clothes, or her friends, or saying cruel, cutting words to members of her family, you may be equally sure that she needs new tubes as well.

It's the failure to get the tubes changed that causes all the trouble.

Why don't we do it? It's very easy, and doesn't cost anything at all. God has promised to do it for us free of charge. Look at that text again. Notice what God says:

"A new heart also will I give you."

That's clear enough, isn't it? And so is the rest.

"A new spirit will I put within you."

"I will take away the stony heart out of your flesh."

"I will give you an heart of flesh."

God's offer is perfectly plain. And it is open for every one of us to accept. All we have to do is to ask Him to work this wonderful change in us, and to do it now.

And if we do, what a change will come over us! Mother won't know us, for sure. And Daddy will hardly be able to believe his ears. There will be such beautiful music—such loving words, such tender sympathy, such gentle answers, such willingness to help and lift and share.

It will pay us a thousandfold to make the change. Life will be so much happier. Everything will seem different then.

Why not do it, and do it now? Jesus is pleading, "My son, My little daughter, give Me thine heart." He wants to take your old heart away and give you a new one. Won't you let Him? Let us pray this little prayer together:

"Saviour, while my heart is tender,
　　I would give that heart to Thee;
All my powers to Thee surrender,
　　Thine and only Thine to be.

"Take me now, Lord Jesus, take me;
　　Let my youthful heart be Thine;
Thy devoted servant make me:
　　Fill my soul with love divine."

When Dick Ran Away

Dick was upset again. In fact, it seemed that he was always getting upset about something. If he did not get his own way all the time, he would carry on in the most ungentlemanly manner. And if anyone corrected him, he would either snarl an angry reply, or else wander off into some corner and sulk.

When in these very bad moods he would mutter threats about running away from home. Although he was only ten years old, he had a very big opinion of himself, and was quite sure that he was well able to look after himself anywhere. That he owed his father and mother anything for all their loving care for him never seemed to enter his mind. He only wanted to get away from all restrictions, away to some place where he would be able to do just as he pleased.

He was thinking these thoughts now. Daddy had asked him to cut the lawn just as he had planned to go out and play ball with the boy next door. How he hated cutting the lawn! Why should he cut the lawn? He wished there were no lawn to cut. He would give anything to get away from the sight of

99

it. But he did cut it, his little soul meanwhile seething with rebellion.

That afternoon his wishes were crossed again. Several times, in fact. As a result he became rude and cross, and finished up with a good spanking and being sent early to bed. He did not say his prayers, and instead of going to sleep, he planned what seemed a glorious dash for liberty. He would get up when everyone else had gone to bed, creep out of the house, and run far, far away. He was not quite sure where he would go, or what he would do when he got there. He had only one all-absorbing desire —to get away where there would be no lawn to cut and where he wouldn't have to give up things for his brothers and sisters, nor be expected to do what he was told.

At last, when all was still, and he felt sure that everyone must be fast asleep, he decided to put his plan into action.

So he crawled softly out of bed, put on his clothes very quietly, took his purse out of the cupboard—he was very proud of this purse, for it contained a whole dollar—and crept silently out of his room.

As he passed the bed where his baby brother was lying asleep, it occurred to him that he would never see little Tiny again, so he bent over and kissed him. A strange lump came into his throat, and he couldn't swallow very well. He kissed

100

Tiny twice, and then went out of the room. Going past the room where Daddy and Mamma were asleep, he thought he would like to say good-by to Mamma anyway. He wasn't quite sure about Daddy, because he had made him cut the lawn. But, really, he wouldn't like not to see Mamma any more.

He began to wonder whether he should run away after all. Then the old, hard spirit came back, and he went downstairs. Very quietly he put on his overcoat and gloves, unlocked the front door, and went out into the cold night air.

He stopped on the doorstep. This was hardly what he had dreamed about. It was too dark for one thing, and too cold for another. Bed began to seem very nice. Perhaps, after all, it would be better to go back.

But no, he wouldn't. He closed the door. There was a snap! and he realized that he couldn't go back now even if he wanted to. That wasn't a nice feeling at all. He wished he hadn't let the door close quite so tightly.

It was done now, however, and he must go. He went down to the front gate and out into the street. There was nobody

about. All was very quiet and still. The sky was black, and the only light came from the street lamps. It was all rather frightening. Dick didn't like it a bit. If the door weren't locked, he told himself, he would go back to bed.

He walked some distance down the street, and as the cold night air cooled his fevered mind, he began to realize more and more what a foolish enterprise he had started on. "If the boys at school get to hear about this," he said to himself, "they will tease me for the rest of the year." The very thought of such a thing made him turn around suddenly and make for home as fast as he could.

He had not gone far, however, when he nearly jumped out of his skin as a heavy hand was laid on his shoulder and a strange voice spoke to him.

"What are you doing out at this time of night?" asked the policeman.

Dick was paralyzed with fright. He had not expected this. Words would not come. He merely struggled to get free.

"You'd better come along with me," said the policeman. "You've been up to some mischief, it seems."

"I haven't, I haven't," gasped Dick. "I've made a mistake, that's all, please, sir."

"I should think you have made a mistake, being out here at one o'clock in the morning. You can tell me all about it when we get down to the station."

"You're not going to take me to the police station, are you?" cried Dick, more frightened still. "Let me go home! I want to go home."

"You'll go home, all right," said the policeman, "after we have had a little chat by the fire."

102

And so poor Dick found himself for the first time in his life on his way to the police station!

There he was asked more questions in ten minutes than any teacher had ever asked him at school. Afterward he was given a very rough mattress to lie on until morning. He didn't sleep at all. He was too frightened, wondering what the policeman was going to do with him and what his daddy would say.

How he wished he had never started out on such a foolish venture! How comfortable his own little bed seemed! And there was no Tiny to look at when he woke up, and no Mamma to come to him when he called. What a night it was!

Morning dawned at last. Very early the policeman came and told him to put his clothes on. Together they walked back home. How very small poor Dick felt! What a home-coming! What would the others say?

Daddy, unshaven and in his pajamas, opened the door. It startled him to see an officer there.

"What in the world!" he began.

The policeman explained and departed, smiling. Dick jumped into Daddy's arms and hugged him, pajamas and all.

They didn't say much to each other, but just walked up the stairs like that to tell Mamma all about it.

For breakfast that morning Mamma gave everybody an egg each in addition to the oatmeal, and opened a new jar of marmalade besides, for she said that, as her little prodigal son had returned, she surely must kill the fatted calf.

And as for Dick, he said very earnestly that he had run away for the last time in his life, and that he certainly wouldn't even think about doing so again.

Preserved From Sickness

Many years ago a mission school in Palestine had a wonderful experience.

Miss Parsons, a good Christian lady, was in charge of the school, and she was very fond of all the little girls under her care.

One day news came that the terrible disease called cholera had broken out in the village, and that many people had already died.

What could the teacher do to save her little girls? There were no doctors near to tell her what to do or to help them if any should become sick. So, not knowing what else to do, the teacher took her trouble to Jesus, who has been called the "Great Physician." She asked Him to protect her mission school, because, after all, it was really His school.

Then she told the little girls about the danger they were in, and together they read the ninety-first psalm every morning and evening while the plague lasted.

Do you know what this beautiful psalm says?

"He that dwelleth in the secret place of the most High

shall abide under the shadow of the Almighty. I will say of the Lord, He is my refuge and my fortress: my God; in Him will I trust. Surely He shall deliver thee from the snare of the fowler, and from the noisome pestilence. He shall cover

thee with His feathers, and under His wings shalt thou trust: His truth shall be thy shield and buckler. Thou shalt not be afraid for the terror by night; nor for the arrow that flieth by day; nor for the pestilence that walketh in darkness; nor for the destruction that wasteth at noonday. A thousand shall fall at thy side, and ten thousand at thy right hand; but it shall not come nigh thee. Only with thine eyes shalt thou behold and see the reward of the wicked. Because thou hast made the Lord, which is my refuge, even the most High, thy habitation; there shall no evil befall thee, neither shall any plague come nigh thy dwelling." Psalm 91:1-10.

The plague became worse; the poor people in the villages around were dying by hundreds. But there in the mission school the teacher and her little girls were claiming the promise, "There shall no evil befall thee, neither shall any plague come nigh thy dwelling."

Jesus kept His word. Not one of those little girls died of the plague, because they had set their love upon Him and had made the Lord their refuge.

The Boy Who Said, "Go On!"

This story is about a cat and how it was saved by a very brave boy.

Well, this poor cat had got lost in London. Perhaps it was the noise, or the crowds of people, or the dozens of streets leading in all directions, that had bewildered her. Anyway, she was lost.

Thinking that if she were to cross the street she might find her way back home, she made a dive into the traffic, dodging here and there and doing her very best to get to the other side. But it was too much for her. She felt as if she

had become a mouse, and all these huge machines were chasing her, determined to kill her if possible.

Oh, dear! What a near thing that was! The wheel of a truck almost grazed her nose.

Whew! A taxicab dashed past, nearly shaving off her whiskers. Would she never get across? Death seemed very near, and nobody seemed to care. She looked this way and that, not knowing whether to go forward or backward, and meanwhile she was sure another truck was coming straight toward her. Someone was shouting, "Get out of the way!" and someone else, "Mind that cat!"

Then suddenly, when she was almost under the wheels of the truck, a little ragged figure jumped toward her, picked her up in his strong arms, and leaped back in a flash onto the sidewalk.

110

He was only a poor newspaper boy, but she felt she loved him very much for his great kindness. No one else had thought of helping her in her desperate need. The boy placed her gently on the sidewalk, and she purred contentedly at his feet.

Just then a big gentleman came up to the boy. He looked as if he must be a lord, or at least a member of Parliament.

"That was a very brave deed, my boy," said he. "I would like you to give me your name and address, for you deserve a medal for this."

"Go on!" said the boy, very much embarrassed.

"I really mean it," said the big gentleman. "Wouldn't you like a medal?"

"Oh no, sir," said the lad, "I could not think of accepting such a thing, for Mother told us we should be kind to animals, and not expect any reward."

And with that the boy turned and bolted, leaving the big gentleman and the poor little pussy staring at each other in surprise!

The Silence Box

What a noisy old place this world is! And it seems to be getting noisier every day. You just can't get peace and quietness anywhere.

Just sit still for a moment, perfectly still, and listen. What noises you can hear!

The radio, of course. Maybe it's playing a lovely tune, and maybe it isn't. It's one of the modern noises we have to put up with. Somebody next door, perhaps, is playing the piano, practicing the five-finger exercises over and over again. Trying on the nerves, isn't it? Somebody else has a phonograph on. Then there's a telephone bell ringing somewhere. Great trucks are lumbering past the front window, and auto horns are tooting.

Nobody seems to want to be quiet any more.

Yet it's nice to be still and quiet, at least every now and then, and wonderfully restful. Lovely thoughts come to the mind at such times, thoughts that somehow can't come at any other time, especially when it's noisy.

Some years ago I visited a great motor repair plant, the huge garage where all of London's motorbuses are overhauled.

112

The noise inside this place is terrific. What a clattering and rattling, what a banging and clanging! Everybody seems to be hammering something. You never heard anything like it in your life. One can hardly hear himself speak, and our guide had to shout to be heard.

Right in the very middle of the plant I noticed a little booth, somewhat like a telephone booth, but larger, with a glass door. Men could be seen working inside, and I wondered what they were doing.

Turning to my guide, I asked him to explain.

"That is the silence box," he said.

"The silence box!" I exclaimed. "What is that? I never heard of such a thing."

"Oh, that's just our name for it," he replied. "You see, when

it comes to the final testing of an engine, we have experts who listen to the rhythm of the motor. There is no other way of being quite sure that everything is all right. Naturally, the men could not hear anything at all out in the main shop; the din is too great; so we have built this silence box in order that in the midst of the noise they can have absolute quiet, and so be able to listen for the slightest defect in the engines."

That set me thinking.

O for a silence box in this noisy life! A place to be still and quiet. A place to listen to these "motors" of ours, and see if they are running smoothly, in harmony with the will of God. A place to listen undisturbed to the voice of the Master Engineer.

Strange, isn't it, but Jesus knew all about the silence box long, long ago.

When telling His disciples how to pray, He said to them: "When thou prayest, enter into thy closet, and when thou hast shut thy door, pray to thy Father which is in secret; and thy Father which seeth in secret shall reward thee openly." Matthew 6:6.

We all need to have a silence box somewhere, you and I and everybody, little children and mothers and fathers, too.

Will you not try to make one for yourself? In the midst of life's hurry and bustle and trouble it will be a wonderful blessing to you.

Mixing in the Love

Mamma was making the Christmas puddings while Freddie and Jimmie looked on. They liked to watch Mamma make Christmas puddings, because she put in such nice things, and every now and then she would give them a raisin or a tiny piece of sugared orange peel.

Mamma said that making the Christmas puddings should be a happy occasion, for it was getting ready for the happiest day of the year. She said that everything she put into the pudding meant something good or kind. The big raisins stood for charity, the little currants for kind thoughts, the flour for friendliness, the butter for good will, the spice for good deeds. Putting in the eggs and milk to bind them all together would be like mixing in the love, Mamma said.

115

Just as Mamma was in the middle of making the pudding, Mrs. Jones called over the fence to ask a favor.

"I'll have to go next door for a few minutes," Mamma said to Freddie and Jimmie, "so mind you be good boys until I come back."

Mamma was away much longer than she expected, and Freddie and Jimmie got tired of waiting. They thought they might just as well help Mamma a little.

"I'm going to stir the pudding for Mamma," said Freddie, getting hold of the big spoon. "I know she'll be so glad to find it all stirred up when she gets back."

"I want to stir it too," said Jimmie, grabbing another spoon.

So Freddie put Jimmie up on the table and the two went to work.

Of course, they stirred the pudding all over the place. Some of it went on their cheeks and noses, and now and then some

of the nice bits went into their mouths. Finding a cupful of egg yolks, Freddie put them in too. He was just trying hard to stir the sticky paste when the back door opened all of a sudden, and in ran Mamma.

"Oh, my dears! what are you doing?" she cried. "Well," said Freddie, quite unconcerned, "we stirred up all the kind thoughts and good deeds, and now we are just mixing in the love."

And, of course, Mamma couldn't say anything to them after that.

The Twins' Evening Prayer

DEAR LORD,

Thank You for a happy day,
And for all the nice things You have given me.
Bless me now and make me a good boy.
Bless all the poor people,
And the sick people in the hospitals.
Bless the missionaries;
Help them to teach lots of boys and girls about Jesus.
Bless dear, dear Daddy and Mamma.
Keep us all safe.
Give me a good sleep all night,
For Jesus' sake. Amen.

The Lighted Way

Fred had been sent on an errand to his uncle's farm. He thought he knew the way well, as it had been described in detail to him by his parents; but as the shades of evening gathered, he began to get a little anxious.

"I should have been there long ago," he said to himself. "I must have taken the wrong road somewhere. I wish someone would come along whom I could ask."

But nobody came, and when darkness fell half an hour later, Fred was standing in the midst of some woods without the faintest idea which way to go.

"Well, I am in a fix," he said to himself. "What shall I do? In this utter darkness I could not find my way back home now, let alone go on to my uncle's farm."

For some minutes he stood still, thinking, and a bit afraid.

"There's one thing I could do," he said to himself by and by, "but I wonder if it will make any difference."

A moment or two later he shut his eyes, put his hands together, and asked Jesus to show him the way out of the woods to his uncle's farm.

118

Lost in the woods, Fred bowed his head, folde his hands, and prayed for guidance.

When he opened his eyes, the first thing he noticed was what seemed to be a path of light through the trees.

"Strange," he thought. "I never saw that before. What does it mean? Anyhow, I'll follow it. I might as well go this way as any other."

So on he went, following the glow of light until at last he was out of the woods. When it ceased, he saw another light in the distance and walked toward it. When he found it came from a farmhouse, he quickened his steps, for he saw it was his uncle's farm.

How happy he was to get there without any mishap, all safe and sound!

"But the path of light in the woods," he said to his uncle, as they talked over his experience that evening, "how did it come to be there?"

"Glowworms," said his uncle, smiling.

And so it was. But God can use even glowworms to answer a little boy's prayer.

A Cry in the Night

Nowadays we are all familiar with radio and television, and all sorts of strange things that nobody had heard of a few years ago. Almost every home has a radio. And what a wonderful thing it is that these little instruments can bring the sound of people's voices to us from hundreds of miles away!

Most of the programs we listen to come from big broadcasting stations in various parts of the country, but occasionally one can hear messages from ships at sea or even from airplanes in flight. The tic-tic-tic that one sometimes hears may possibly be one ship talking to another in Morse code. People who understand this code can sometimes learn what one captain is saying to another.

Some time ago there was a man in the south of England who made it his hobby to listen to these messages from ships. Long after the big broadcasting stations had closed down for the night, he would go on listening, picking up one ship after another.

Then one stormy night his aerial was blown down. He

121

H. BAERG

might have left it down and gone to bed. But no, he was so keen about his hobby that he went out in the dark, climbed the fir tree at the end of his garden, fixed up the wire as best he could, and went back to his radio again.

Hardly had he begun to tune in than he became aware of the persistent call of S O S, the universal signal of a ship in distress. This, he thought, was interesting indeed, and well worth the trouble he had taken to fix his aerial. The call continued, S O S—S O S—S O S.

Suddenly it dawned upon him that the call was not being answered. Of course, he told himself, that was why it was being repeated so continuously. Could it be, then, that he was the only one listening to this cry for help?

Just then, in broken English, came this urgent and piteous appeal:

"Please, everybody come and help."

The man jumped to his feet and ran to the telephone. Ringing up the nearest radio station, he asked if they had heard the call. They had not. He begged them to listen. They agreed. Messages were sent out, asking other ships to stop signaling for a time. At once the cry of the little ship was heard. Immediately help was sent, and the ship was saved.

An hour after telephoning to the radio station the man's aerial was blown down again. It had stayed up just long enough for the signal of distress to be heard!

Strange, wasn't it? Often the providence of God works with humble means to accomplish His purposes.

And just as this lonely man with his little homemade radio was able to bring help to that storm-tossed ship, while the big station was too busy to hear its cry, so little children, small though they are, may hear many a cry in the night from sad and suffering souls, and by kind and loving deeds bring help and blessing to these "ships" in distress.

H. BAERG

Sticking Pins Into Billy

Master William Croker, known to the other boys in the town as "Billy," was a very bright lad, but he had one fault. He thought so much of himself that his hat would hardly go on his head.

Billy's skill in games made him a natural leader of the boys, but they all secretly disliked him because he was always bragging about the wonderful things he could do. He never had time to listen to what the other boys had to say, but would always interrupt them with an account of some experience he had had. If someone said he had seen a big frog, Billy would say, "That's nothing; last week I saw a frog much bigger than that."

At last the other boys became tired of his boasting, and be-

125

gan to talk over ways and means of putting an end to it. As Tommy Walters said, Billy was swollen up with pride as big as a balloon, and it was high time somebody stuck a nice big pin into him.

But how to do it was another question. Some of the boys suggested ducking him in the river; but Billy was quite a strong boy, and none of the others wanted to take the risk of a personal quarrel with him. Then Tommy struck on a bright idea.

"I know of something better than that," he said. "It wouldn't be kind to put him in the river, and it wouldn't do him much good anyhow. Have you ever thought what is the matter with Billy?"

The others crowded around. "No, what?" they asked. They were in a good mood to try anything.

"I'll tell you. You've all noticed how Billy seems to win all our games," said Tommy. "That's the trouble with him; he thinks we're no good, and that he can always beat us. I'm tired of his superior airs. If we are going to stop his bragging, we must learn to play better ourselves."

"Pretty good sense," said another boy. "If we could make Billy lose every game for a few weeks, he would soon change his tune."

"You're right," said Tommy, "but it's up to us to beat him. Why not practice some of our games on the quiet, and surprise Billy?"

"But we can't all win,"

said a pale-faced, frightened youngster; "and I don't see how we can practice all the games we play."

"Goose!" said Tommy. "Of course we cannot all practice everything at once. No; but let one or two practice running, some jumping, and others marbles. I'm going to practice so I can throw him out at first base the next time we play."

"Hurrah!" laughed the others. "Let's do it."

Tommy's idea certainly did put new life into those boys. Their mothers and teachers soon began to wonder what was the matter with them, for nearly all of them began to practice hard at the game they had chosen in their "secret" meeting.

Billy, too, noticed it but did not suspect that all this effort was directed against him. As the days went by, he began to notice the results of the plan. Whereas in running races he had been able to keep an easy lead, 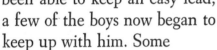 a few of the boys now began to keep up with him. Some passed him, and

instead of always winning, he learned what it means to lose.

When the school sports day came around, so many pins were stuck into Billy that he was reduced to almost normal size. Billy had not bothered to practice for any of the events because he felt so certain of success. The other boys, however, had worked very hard, with but one purpose in view, and they won. Poor Billy did not win a single race.

He felt very bad about it, but was sure he would be able to regain his lost reputation at the baseball game which was to follow the field events, for he prided himself on being a very good hitter.

This ball game was always a big affair, at least in the boys' eyes, for it was held on the town diamond, and usually there were many spectators.

Billy was up first. He told the boys that he was going to make at least ten runs, and that they had better keep their eye on the town clock, for he was going to hit a ball right in the middle of it. Then, carrying his bat with a real swagger, he strolled across the field as though he were a professional. But much to his surprise, Billy fanned out.

In the next inning Tommy was

up first. He saw at once that his great opportunity had come. After all he had said to the other boys, he knew what he must do.

Now, Tommy had been practicing batting and fielding every morning and evening. In the morning, before his father went to work, Tommy would get him out into the vacant lot next to the house to pitch him a few balls. After school he would get one of the boys to play with him. Then in the evening, after supper, his father would throw him a few more, until his eye and timing were nearly perfect, and he could hit curves as hard as straight balls. So now he really felt ready for the big game.

Tommy walked out to the batter's box with more assurance than ever before. The pitcher shot him a fast ball. But Tommy was ready; he had been training his eye carefully, and he was sure of his swing. To the surprise of all, he hit the ball away out, and before the left fielder recovered the ball, Tommy was rounding third. The left fielder threw to Billy, who was catching, but Billy dropped the ball, and Tommy slid in home —a home run.

Tommy made two more home runs that day, one in the last inning with two out and two men on bases, partly

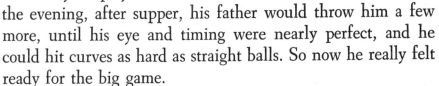

4-9

because Billy, who was really a good player, lost his nerve at being surpassed, and partly because he worked so hard to succeed. Billy failed to make a single run in the game.

At the close of the game they all crowded around Tommy and proclaimed him the hero of the day.

As for Billy, no one would have thought he was the same boy who had walked so confidently onto the diamond a couple of hours before.

"How about the town clock?" piped a small voice.

"And how about those ten runs?" ventured a bolder voice among the boys.

But Billy only walked away with his head down. That was the last "pin" that Billy needed to have stuck into him. No one ever heard him boasting again.

Four Jars of Jam

Tubby and Toby had just returned home from the big city. They were very much excited and very tired, though they wouldn't admit it, for they had spent the whole day with Mamma, walking around a wonderful exhibition. It had been such fun! They had seen so many interesting things that when they started to tell Daddy about them they got all mixed up.

Then they began to bring out the treasures they had gathered during the day. Both of them had a collection of the most delightful little samples you could wish to see—tiny pieces of cheese wrapped in silver paper, packages of cookies and cornflakes, and best of all, four dainty little jars of jam.

Oh, those jars of jam! What shrieks of delight greeted their unpacking! How pretty they looked, standing on the table with the light shining through them. One was strawberry jam, one apricot jam, one black currant jelly, and the other marmalade. Tubby and Toby took quite a long time to decide how the four jars should be divided, but at last Tubby agreed to have the strawberry and the apricot, and Toby took the black currant

131

jelly and the marmalade. Each face wore a happy smile.

Fancy having two whole jars of jam each! It seemed too wonderful to be true. Tubby and Toby stood them up beside their plates at suppertime, so they could keep their eyes on them. Of course, they were not very big jars, but to the happy, excited eyes of Tubby and Toby they were more precious than the biggest jars in Mamma's store cupboard.

All through suppertime they talked about these four treasured jam jars—how they got them, and what they were going

132

to do with them. They were quite sure that they were going to eat all the jam themselves, and that, if they only tasted a spoonful every day, the jars would last for weeks and weeks.

Supper was almost over when Daddy said something that rather upset things a bit.

"Poor old Dad!" he said, talking as though to himself in a very disconsolate tone of voice. "Poor old Dad! He never has a jam jar all to himself. Nobody ever gives him anything. Poor old Dad!"

Tubby and Toby stopped talking. They both looked at Daddy in surprise, questioning in their little minds whether he really meant what he said. Then they looked at their precious jam jars.

"Here, Daddy," said Tubby, "have my jar of strawberry jam."

"You darling boy!" said Daddy. "I don't want to take your jam. It was only fun."

"But you must have it," said Tubby, setting the jar of strawberry jam down with a bang in front of Daddy's plate. "You see, I still have the apricot left."

Daddy nearly shed a tear at this, but he didn't because he was too busy watching Toby out of the corner of his eye.

The struggle was harder for Toby. He was breathing very deeply, and looking hard first at one jar and then at the other. He picked up the marmalade, put it down, then picked up the black currant jelly. His solemn little face showed that a big battle was being fought inside.

"Daddy," he said at last, "I think I will let you have one of mine as well. You can have this jar of black currant jelly."

And with that Toby plumped the jar of black currant jelly down beside Daddy's plate.

"You dear, precious boys," said Daddy. "Of course I won't eat your lovely jam; but I am pleased you gave it to me. I shall remember it forever and ever. And now I think I shall have to see what I can find."

And then Daddy started fumbling in his left-hand trouser pocket, making a sort of jingling noise that Tubby and Toby had heard before and knew so well!

134

"Honour thy father and thy mother: that thy days may be long upon the land which the Lord thy God giveth thee."

Exodus 20:12

Doreen's Jewel Box

Five Minutes to Ten

Just one more week, and it would be Doreen's birthday. To think of it! She would be ten years old. Mamma said she was just "five minutes to ten."

Doreen felt she was now quite grown up, and that it was time she had some "grown-up" presents. Indeed, she was not at all backward in saying out loud what she was expecting.

"You see, Mamma," she would say, "my tricycle is much too small for me now, and don't you think I really ought to have a small girl's bicycle?"

137

Doreen reminded her mother that there was just one more week before her birthday.

Then a little later, "Mamma, when I'm ten I think I should have a doll's house big enough to get inside; you know, the kind you open at the front, with real stairs and fireplaces and electric lights."

And then, "Oh, yes, Mamma, and I simply must have a new outfit of clothes for my big doll—all silk this time."

To all of which Mamma listened patiently, explaining that she really hadn't any money this year, and that it took all she had to buy food and clothes for the family.

But Doreen didn't seem to hear.

"You know, Mamma," she went on, "when I'm ten I should like a pretty jewel case with some pearls in it."

"Whatever next!" exclaimed Mamma, looking up from her knitting. "Whoever put that idea into your little head?"

"Well, Kittie Naylor's got a whole string of pearls that she wears at parties, and big people wear them, and princesses."

"But it isn't the jewels that make people princesses," said Mother. "And as for Kittie Naylor's pearls, they are made of plastic."

"Then they can't cost very much," said Doreen.

"That may be," said Mamma, "but my little girl surely does not want to go about wearing a sham. There's nothing makes a

girl look so cheap as imitation jewelry. It's the worst kind of pretense."

"Well, then, can't I have a string of real pearls?"

"My dear Doreen! They would cost more than everything in this house. Pearls are very expensive. But apart from the expense, people who really love Jesus do not wear pearls."

"Why not?"

"Because the Bible tells us not to." (1 Timothy 2:9.)

"Oh dear!" sighed Doreen. "It seems as if I can't have anything now. I wish I weren't going to have a birthday at all."

"Oh, don't say that," said Mamma. "I shouldn't be a bit surprised if something would turn up between now and then to make you happy."

"My new bicycle?" cried Doreen eagerly.

"I don't think it could be that," said Mamma. "It would cost too much. But, let me see, if you are very anxious for a jewel box, I might talk with your daddy about that."

"Oh, do!" exclaimed Doreen. "I should love one so much."

"Well, we'll see," said Mamma with a smile.

Ten O'clock

Doreen pushed down the bedclothes, sat up, and rubbed her eyes.

It was still quite dark, but she was awake enough to know that the great morning for which she had been longing so much had come at last.

She peered around the room. There was no bicycle and no doll's house. "Downstairs perhaps," she said to herself.

She put out her hand and felt for the chair beside her bed. Ah, what was this? A flat, brown-paper package, tied up with string. She drew it very carefully into bed beside her,

142

and her heart beat faster at every rustle of the brown paper.

Lying down again, Doreen decided to enjoy the "feel" of the parcel until there was daylight enough to open it. Meanwhile she tried to imagine what might be inside.

She felt sure it must be the long-desired jewel box. It was just the right size and shape. She pictured a very handsome case filled with sparkling diamonds and emeralds and gleaming jewels of many shapes and colors. Shaking the parcel, she expected to hear the gems rattle together. But there was no sound. "Of course," she said to herself, "how stupid I am!

If they are precious jewels they will be wrapped up in tissue paper, or set in golden rings on velvet cushions."

Morning dawned at last. Jumping up, Doreen put on her clothes, with one eye all the time on the brown-paper parcel. She had decided to keep the pleasure of opening it until she went downstairs.

Dressed at last, she went down to the dining room. There was no bicycle or doll's house there. Evidently Mamma had spent all her money on the jewel box, thought Doreen.

Snip! snip! went the scissors, and off fell the string

143

and the first sheet of brown paper. What a moment of suspense!

There was some writing on the next piece of wrapping paper. Doreen's eyes opened wider than ever as she read the words:

"DOREEN'S JEWEL BOX"

"Hurrah!" she shouted, hastily tearing off the next sheet of paper. Underneath was a beautiful cardboard box of a mottled-green color. "How pretty!" she exclaimed, slowly and very carefully lifting the lid. She peeped inside.

Then something happened.

"Oh!" cried Doreen, stamping her little foot and flinging the box across the room. "It's not a jewel box! It's not a jewel box!"

Crash! went a flowerpot.

"Whatever is the matter?" cried Mamma, running into the room.

"It's not a jewel box! It's not a jewel box!" sobbed Doreen, "and you said it was a jewel box. It isn't. It's just a horrid, nasty, ugly old book, and I don't like books, and I don't want a book—and you said it was a jewel box, and it isn't, and—and——"

"Now come, come, Doreen," said Mamma. "You mustn't take on like this. You must have got out of bed on the wrong side today, and on your birthday, too!"

"But you said I should have a jewel box——"

"And we have given you one," said Mamma.

"You haven't; it's only a nasty, horrid, ugly old book!"

"No, no, Doreen. Have you looked inside it yet?"

"No."

"Then you have cried too soon. You will find that it is a

144

most extraordinary jewel box, packed full of the richest gems."

Doreen began to dry her tears.

"Daddy and I," said Mamma, "have spent lots of money on this jewel box, and if you look after it, you will have it all your life. When you are grown up you will still be telling people about the lovely jewel box you were given on your tenth birthday."

"But where are the jewels?" asked Doreen.

"You must go and look for them," said Mother. "I will help you find some of them later on."

Doreen's curiosity was aroused, and she walked across the room to pick up the mottled-green box.

"I'm sorry I knocked your plant over," she said.

"Yes, that is too bad," said Mamma, "but I will sweep up the mess this time if you will start looking for those jewels."

Picking up the box, Doreen kissed Mamma and went quietly upstairs to her room.

Seeking Goodly Pearls

Why, it's a Bible!" said Doreen to herself as she carefully lifted the Book out of the box. "And to think that I threw it across the room like that!

"And what a beauty it is!" she went on. "Look at the gold edges with the red shining through! And what thin paper and lovely leather! It's just like a jewel box, anyway."

Inside, on the first blank page, Doreen read her name and the following message:

"To our darling Doreen on her tenth birthday, with love from Mamma and Daddy."

147

Underneath this presentation was a text of Scripture:

"Acquaint now thyself with Him, and be at peace: thereby good shall come unto thee. Receive, I pray thee, the law from His mouth, and lay up His words in thine heart." Job 22: 21, 22.

Doreen ran downstairs. "Mamma dear, have I found the first jewel?"

Mamma smiled. "I believe you have," she said.

"But how can I find some more?" asked Doreen.

"Why not look for a string of pearls?" said Mamma. "And while you are looking for those, you may come across diamonds, sapphires, rubies, emeralds, and other precious stones."

"But how shall I find them?" asked Doreen.

"Oh, you won't find them all at once," said Mamma, "but put them down on a piece of paper as you come across them. Keep on the lookout for beautiful texts and sentences begining with P. They will do for pearls. Those beginning with R will do for rubies, E for emeralds, and D for diamonds. See?"

"Yes," said Doreen, "what a lovely idea!"

"I can think of a pearl," said Mamma.

"Tell me," said Doreen.

"It is in the fourteenth chapter of John," said Mamma. " 'Peace I leave with you, My peace I give unto you.' John 14:27. Then there's another beautiful pearl: 'Perfect love casteth out fear.' 1 John 4:18."

"I know one," said Doreen. "Praise ye the Lord!"

"That's right," said Mamma. "There's a whole string of those pearls in the Psalms. You must see how many of them you can find. Open your jewel box to Psalm 112 or 113."

Very carefully Doreen opened her beautiful new Bible,

149

Doreen held her Bible close and recalled all the beautiful promises she had learned.

turning the thin leaves as if they were made of gold. "Yes," she cried eagerly, "I can see two, three, four pearls all at once!" Then a moment or two later, "I've found another. Listen, Mamma; this is a beautiful jewel."

"Read it to me," said Mamma.

" 'Pleasant words are as an honeycomb, sweet to the soul, and health to the bones.' "

"Yes," said Mamma. "That is beautiful indeed. And don't you think that this sort of jewel box is really much more lovely

than one filled with just ordinary pearls and diamonds? They
would sparkle and shine and seem very pretty while we looked
at them in the box, but we would have to shut them up and
put them away. But these jewels from this wonderful Book we
can carry about with us all day long, and they become more
and more beautiful the longer we look at them."

"Yes, Mamma," said Doreen, "they sort of go on sparkling
in our heads afterward, don't they?"

"I believe you are right," said Mamma with a smile.

Doreen closed her Bible, clasped it to her heart, and carried it into the parlor, where she placed it on the table under
the reading lamp.

Diamonds and Rubies

Of course Doreen had to go to school the next day, and it was not until evening that she was able to spend any more time looking for the precious gems in her jewel box.

She smiled happily as she helped her mother wash the supper dishes.

"Shall we try to find some other jewels tonight?" she asked. "I think I would like to look for some rubies. You must help me, for I don't know just where to start."

"Oh, yes, you know where to find one," said Mamma. "Surely you can think of the verse that begins with an *R*— 'Re—mem—' "

"I know," cried Doreen. " 'Remember the Sabbath day, to keep it holy.' "

"That's right," said Mamma. "And can't you think of another 'remember'? The minister spoke of it at church the other day."

"Do you mean, 'Remember now thy Creator in the days of thy youth'?"

"Of course, that's the one," said Mamma. "What a lot of beautiful rubies we are finding! I can think of another. 'Resist the devil, and he will flee from you.' James 4:7."

"What does that mean?" asked Doreen.

"That means that when we are tempted to do anything that we know to be wrong, we are to say No! very firmly, just as if we were speaking straight to the great tempter himself. And if we say No! he will run away, and we shall be sure to do right."

Doreen hung the dish towel up to dry, and went skipping into the parlor for her Bible. Curling up in the window seat, she opened her jewel box with gentle hands lest she rumple a single one of its beautiful pages. Soon she found Psalm 37, where Mamma had said she would find more rubies.

"Oh, listen, Mamma," she cried as her mother entered the room. "This chapter has diamonds in it too. Here is a lovely

153

one, 'Delight thyself also in the Lord; and He shall give thee the desires of thine heart.' "

"That is a glorious diamond indeed," said Mamma, "and if you will read the margin of the next verse you will find that this diamond is set in a ring with a ruby."

Doreen had never bothered to look in the margin before,

Remember now thy Creator in the days of thy youth.

ECCL. 12:1

but this time she quickly saw what Mamma meant. "I see," she cried. "In the margin it says, 'Roll thy way upon the Lord; trust also in Him; and He shall bring it to pass.' "

"Yes," said Mamma, "we would never have any worries if we always remember that we possess these two precious jewels."

"Why, here is still another ruby in this same chapter!" exclaimed Doreen, reading on. " 'Rest in the Lord, and wait patiently for Him.' What does that mean?"

"Almost the same as the other texts," said Mamma. "Jesus does not want us to worry about anything. If we do not get all that we think we want immediately, we are not to fret and pout about it, but leave it with Him and trust Him to give us what is best for us."

"Does that include bicycles and dolls' houses, too, Mamma?" asked Doreen with half a smile.

"Why, yes, of course it does, darling. And, really, it's the quickest and best way to get anything we desire. If we will tell Jesus we want it ever so badly, He will see that we get it just as soon as He sees it will be good for us. That is what it means to 'rest in the Lord, and wait patiently for Him.' Sometimes it means waiting a long time, but if we continue to *rest* in Him, the time will soon pass. Then afterward, when we at last have what we desired, we shall be ever so glad that we didn't have it any sooner."

"Well," sighed Doreen, "this certainly is a wonderful chapter to have two rubies and one diamond all in seven verses."

"I should think it is," said Mamma. "It is one of my favorite chapters in the whole Bible."

Emeralds

The evening sun and mist were filling the sky with glorious colors.

"Mamma!" cried Doreen. "Come and see the lovely rainbow!"

"How beautiful!" exclaimed Mamma, as she came out on the front porch. "It's the brightest one I think I ever saw."

"All those colors make me think of my jewel box," said Doreen.

"What a good idea!" said Mamma. "The sky is one great jewel box this evening."

156

"Do you see the green in the rainbow, Mamma? Are there any pretty green jewels?"

"Yes, emeralds are among our most precious gems," agreed Mamma. "And there are beautiful emeralds in your jewel box. Can you think of a Scripture text beginning with an *E*? There are several of them. Perhaps you will remember the one about eyes and ears."

"Oh, yes, I know that," said Doreen. "You mean 'Eye hath not seen, nor ear heard'?" 1 Corinthians 2:9.

"Yes, is not that a glorious emerald?" said Mamma. "It tells us that Jesus is preparing a home for us in heaven more beautiful than anything we have seen or heard of or even imagined. We can think of the most lovely places where we have been for our vacations—by the seaside, with cliffs and caves, mountains and valleys, trees and flowers—and then know that heaven will be ten thousand times more beautiful still. This glorious emerald gives us just a tiny glimpse of what Jesus is planning to do for us by and by. Now let us find another. I can think of one, can you?"

"No, do tell me yours."

"You know it well; it is very much like the other: 'Every good gift and every perfect gift is from above.' James 1:17."

"Fancy your remembering them so well, Mamma!"

"But you must remember them, too," replied Mamma. "You should be writing down where all these precious jewels are found, so that you will be able to find them again and share them with others."

"I am doing that, Mamma," said Doreen.

"And that last emerald we thought of is one we should wear every day, for it reminds us that all the good things we

157

Eye hath not seen, nor ear heard, neither have entered into the heart of man, the things which God hath prepared for them that love Him.

I CORINTHIANS 2:9

enjoy—home, food, clothing, sunshine, fresh air, and good health—are given to us by Jesus."

"Isn't there a text somewhere that begins something like this, 'Examine me, O Lord, and prove me'?" asked Doreen.

"Yes," said Mamma. "That is another emerald, and you will find it in the Psalms. It is a little prayer that God will look into our hearts and tell us if there is anything there that He does not like."

"But what do the words 'prove me' mean?" Doreen looked puzzled.

"Well," said Mamma, "they mean 'test me,' or 'try me.' You have tests and examinations at school every few weeks, but we should ask God to examine us every day."

"Do you think He would give me an A grade?" asked Doreen with a little smile.

"Sometimes," said Mamma, "but not every day, I'm afraid.

"Go and get your Bible, dear, for there is an emerald in the thirtieth chapter of Proverbs I want you to read, but I can't remember the verse."

Doreen returned quickly with her Bible and had no trouble finding the book of Proverbs. She had not read many verses before she cried happily, "Here it is, Mamma. 'Every word of God is pure.'"

"That's the one," said Mamma. "Now read Psalm 12, verse 6. This is not an 'emerald,' but it throws a beam of light on the one you have just found, and makes it gleam still more brightly."

Doreen turned to the Psalms. Then she read, " 'The words of the Lord are pure words: as silver tried in a furnace of earth, purified seven times.' "

159

"Now we can see how we can make our words as pure and lovely as the words of God," said Mamma.

"But Mamma, I don't understand what you mean," said Doreen.

"Well, we should put all our thoughts through a fiery furnace seven times before we speak once."

"Oh, my! We wouldn't say very much then."

"Perhaps not," said Mamma. "And that might be all the better for us. Now I'll tell you how to do it.

"First of all, before we speak we should ask ourselves, 'Is it kind?' That is the first time through the fire. Then, 'Is it necessary?' That would burn a good many words. Then, 'Is it truthful?' After that, put it in the fire again and ask, 'Is it courteous?' If it is still not burned up, ask, 'Is it friendly?' Then, 'Is it helpful?' And then, if there is still anything left, ask, 'Would I like someone to say it to me?'"

"Oh, dear!" exclaimed Doreen, "I'm sure I could never remember to ask all those questions every time."

"Perhaps not," said Mamma, "but it would be a good thing to ask as many as you can before you speak. It would save many heartaches and tears. Don't you think so?"

"Suppose so," said Doreen.

"Now I see it's getting quite late," said Mamma. "Kiss me good night, dearie. Tomorrow night we shall start searching for sapphires."

Searching for Sapphires

Doreen was so quiet upstairs that Mamma thought she must be asleep. She tiptoed up to her room and found her copying Bible texts in her little notebook.

"See, Mamma," she cried, "I have found several emeralds since yesterday."

Mamma took the book and read: " 'Every good gift and every perfect gift is from above, and cometh down from the Father of lights, with whom is no variableness, neither shadow of turning.' James 1:17."

"And I have another one here," said Doreen.

" 'Even a child is known by his doings, whether his work be pure, and whether it be right.' "

4-11   161

"That's a very good one," said Mamma. "Now would you like to start some pages for other jewels?"

"Oh, yes," said Doreen, "I want to fill up my notebook."

"Then let us begin with sapphires. There are scores of them hidden in our wonderful jewel box. Can you think of one in the twenty-third psalm?"

Doreen thought for a moment or two, trying to recall the words of the "shepherd psalm."

"Yes, I remember," she said. "You mean the last verse: 'Surely goodness and mercy shall follow me all the days of my life.'"

"That's the one," said Mamma. "Lend me your Bible a minute, and I will show you another close to it. There it is, in Psalm 20, verse 7: 'Some trust in chariots and some in horses: but we will remember the name of the Lord our God.' Isn't that beautiful? You will find still another in Psalm 90,

The Lord is my shepherd; I shall not want · · · · ·

SURELY GOODNESS AND MERCY SHALL FOLLOW ME ALL THE DAYS OF MY LIFE

verse 12. I am sure you know that one well: 'So teach us to number our days, that we may apply our hearts unto wisdom.' "

"Oh, yes, I know that one," said Doreen, "but I'm not quite sure what it means."

"It is very simple. We each have just so long to live, but nobody knows how long that may be. So God says to us, 'Make the most of each passing day.' If we are at school, He wants us to study hard to get ready for the work He may have for us to do in years to come. He doesn't want us to idle away any time in daydreaming or foolish talking. He knows we shall be much happier if we keep busy as though every minute cost money."

"I want a sapphire from the New Testament," said Doreen.

"Think hard, dear, and see if you can tell me if there were

163

any sapphires in the lovely jewels of truth that fell from the Saviour's lips."

"'Suffer the little children to come unto Me, and forbid them not: for of such is the kingdom of God.' Mark 10:14."

"Yes, that's right."

"I will tell you another," said Mother. "You remember the words: 'Seek ye first the kingdom of God, and His right-eousness; and all these things shall be added unto you.' And we might call this 'sapphire corner,' for packed right close up to this is another: 'Sufficient unto the day is the evil thereof.' And just across the page is yet one more: 'Son, be of good cheer; thy sins be forgiven thee.'

"So you see, dear, the whole Bible is strewn from end to end with precious jewels. And we have scarcely begun to find them."

DOREEN'S JEWEL BOX

Prayer Jewels

O ne of the girls at school has a beautiful bracelet set with many lovely gems," Doreen remarked as she was eating her lunch next day. "Why can't I have a bracelet like that, Mamma?"

"Well, Doreen, you know the Bible tells us not to adorn ourselves with 'gold, or pearls, or costly array.' 1 Timothy 1:9. Wearing jewelry often makes people vain. The Bible also reminds us that our bodies are the temple of the Holy Spirit, and if we live pure, sweet lives like Jesus, we shall shine with far greater beauty than the costliest ring or bracelet could possibly give us."

165

"Didn't God say He would write His law in our hearts?" asked Doreen. "What does that mean?"

"It means to remember His law and love it so that we will never break His commandments," answered Mamma. "And we can wear the jewels of His Word in our hearts so that they will always shine out in our conduct."

"Oh, then, a bracelet of emeralds or rubies from my jewel box would please Jesus," said Doreen happily. She wanted to begin making Scripture jewelry right away.

"First let us make a bracelet of prayer jewels," said Mamma. "Let us imagine that we have a beautiful gold bracelet ready to be set with precious stones. What kind of stones shall we put in it?"

"Let's mix them," said Doreen. "I should like to put in a pearl and a ruby."

"Very well. And I should like to put in an emerald and a topaz and an amethyst and perhaps one or two others."

"How will the colors blend?" asked Doreen.

"I'm not quite sure about that," said Mamma. "We should have a red ruby, a green emerald, a greenish-yellow topaz, a creamy pearl, and a purple amethyst. I think we need a diamond to brighten it up a bit."

"So do I," said Doreen. "But I'm still afraid we shall not make very good jewelers."

"Well, you wait and see," said Mamma. "First we have to sort out our jewels. Shall we find the topaz first? You will see one at the end of Proverbs 15, verse 8. Will you look for it?"

Doreen opened her Bible at the book of Proverbs and soon found the familiar words, " 'The prayer of the upright is His delight.' "

166

"I think," said Mamma, "that this will make a beautiful gem to put into our prayer bracelet. It tells us that Jesus loves to hear our prayers. Just as a Mother loves to listen to her baby talking to her, so Jesus delights to hear His children talking to Him. And the more we speak to Him the happier He is. Don't you think that is a lovely topaz to begin with?"

"Yes," said Doreen. "Now let us find your emerald."

"My emerald is found in Psalm 55, verse 17," said Mamma. "You will soon see how beautifully it goes with the topaz. Read it for me, please."

Our Father which art in heaven, Hallowed be thy name. Thy kingdom come. Thy will be done in earth, as it is in heaven. Give us this day our daily bread. And forgive us our debts, as we forgive our debtors. And lead us not into temptation, but deliver us from evil: For thine is the kingdom, and the power, and the glory, for ever. Amen.

H. BAERG

Doreen read, " 'Evening and morning, and at noon, will I pray, and cry aloud: and He shall hear my voice.' "

"This tells us," said Mamma, "how often we should remember to speak to Jesus. Of course we always say our prayers in the evening, before we go to bed, but we should also say them in the morning, as soon as we get up. Before we speak to anyone else we should kneel down by our beds and speak to Jesus and ask Him to bless and keep us through the day. Then, besides that, we should spare just a little while at lunch time to think of Him too."

"I don't think I could do that," said Doreen. "There's always such a rush."

"I know," said Mamma, "but let us try hard. We shall be so much happier if we do. Now we must have your pearl. Will you read the seventeenth verse of the fifth chapter of First Thessalonians?"

"Oh, that book is so hard to find!" said Doreen, as she fumbled about with the pages.

"That book will be easier to find if you remember that it is almost exactly in the middle of the New Testament, just after Colossians."

"Oh, I have it now. Here it is, and it is a short one, easy to remember. 'Pray without ceasing.' "

"Now our bracelet is beginning to look very pretty," said Mamma. "We have learned that Jesus delights to hear us pray, that we are to pray three times a day, and now that we are to 'pray without ceasing.' "

"Well, we couldn't do that," said Doreen.

"No, I don't think we could pray all day long. It doesn't mean that. It means that when we want something very badly,

169

we must keep on praying for it. We mustn't stop praying just because it doesn't come all at once. And we are not to let ourselves get so busy that we haven't time to pray. Now let us put in the amethyst. Can you think of one?"

Once more Doreen turned over the pages of her precious Book. "I have it," she said: " 'All things, whatsoever ye shall ask in prayer, believing, ye shall receive.' "

"That is the brightest jewel we have found tonight," said Mamma. "It's such a big promise. Just think of a storekeeper saying to you at Christmas time, 'You can have anything you like out of this window.' Wouldn't that make you happy! But that is just what Jesus says here. We can have anything He thinks is good for us just for the asking. The only condition is that we shall believe we are going to get it! Isn't that a wonderful promise for Him to make?

"Now for a ruby. What would you say to putting in the words of the dying thief on the cross: 'Remember me when Thou comest into Thy kingdom'?"

"Yes," said Doreen, "I think that's very nice, but what shall we do for our diamond?"

"I believe there is one in the Lord's Prayer," said Mamma.

" 'Deliver us from evil.' " The words fairly popped out of Doreen's mouth.

"And now our prayer bracelet is complete," said Mamma. "Of course we could add many more stones equally precious, but these give us our first piece of jewelry, glittering with many-colored gems. I'm sure you did not think there was a bracelet like this in your jewel box a few days ago, did you?"

170

DOREEN'S JEWEL BOX

A Locket of Love

I have been wondering what kind of jewelry we might put together tonight," said Mamma. "How would you like to set some of our precious stones in a golden locket?"

"I think that would be lovely," said Doreen. "Lockets are so pretty, especially those heart-shaped ones."

"Well, we will imagine this is heart-shaped, if you like,

171

"Children, obey your parents in the Lord: for this is right."

and then we shall think we are setting all these jewels in your own heart."

"But what is the subject?" asked Doreen.

"Something, surely, that can be written on a heart," said Mamma. "We might begin with a chalcedony, one that is a commandment, for you remember the Lord said He would write His laws in our hearts. You will find a beautiful one in the very first verse of the sixth chapter of Ephesians."

Doreen looked up the verse and read, " 'Children, obey your parents in the Lord: for this is right.' "

"Of course we couldn't leave this out of such a locket, could we?" said Mamma. "I think it is just as well to have this bright-green stone right in the center of the other jewels. You see, Doreen, if only children would always do what their parents tell them to do, right at once, it would save such a lot of trouble and tears, wouldn't it?"

Doreen sat very still and quiet till Mamma had finished. She remembered that there had been several times lately when she had not obeyed as quickly as she should have done. At the first opportunity she changed the subject. "What other jewel shall we put in the locket, Mamma?" she asked.

"An onyx will go well with a chalcedony, and I see one in my concordance here that ought to fit nicely. Read Deuteronomy 5, verse 29."

Doreen found the place and read as follows: " 'O that there were such an heart in them, that they would fear Me, and keep all My commandments always, that it might be well with them, and with their children for ever!' "

"I love that verse," said Mamma. "It shows us how we can always be sure of having God's blessing with us. If we

173

The happiest children in the world are those who
    obey when their parents call.

will but love Him and keep all His commandments *always*, He will see that all is well with us and with our children forever. My mother wanted things to go well with me, so she kept God's commandments; I want things to go well with you, darling, so I try to keep God's commandments; and, of course, I want to see you do the same as you grow up.

"Now, there's another glorious amethyst in the very next chapter of Deuteronomy which fits in with this, and really should be included in our golden locket tonight. It's verse 24. Read it, dear."

Doreen read, " 'And the Lord commanded us to do all these statutes, to fear the Lord our God, for our good always, that He might preserve us alive, as it is at this day.' "

"So you see, dear, God's greatest reason for giving us the Ten Commandments was 'for our good always.' He is always thinking of our good. Fathers and Mothers often have to tell their children .to do certain things and not to do other things, but it is only for their good, to keep them from making mistakes that might bring them sorrow. So it is with God. He wants His children to be happy. He tells them to keep the seventh day as the Sabbath, and not to do any work on that day. He tells them not to kill and not to steal. We may not understand all His reasons for such commandments, but we can only be truly happy, and receive His full blessing, as we keep them. We must keep *all* His commandments *always* if it is to be well with us and with our children.

"But we must find a few more jewels quickly, or it will be too late to finish our locket tonight. I think we should have a topaz in it, don't you? There is one in Matthew 5, verses 17 and 18. You read it."

Again Doreen read, this time from the words of Jesus in His Sermon on the Mount: " 'Think not that I am come to destroy the law. . . . Till heaven and earth pass away, one jot or one tittle shall in no wise pass from the law, till all be fulfilled.'

"Why," said Doreen, "there are two verses with a topaz right together!"

"Yes," said Mamma, "and they are both so valuable we must certainly put them both into our locket. It is quite clear what they mean. Jesus did not change any part of the commandments when He came to the world, and they never will be changed 'till heaven and earth pass.' So that makes it clear that Jesus expects everyone to keep the Ten Commandments

175

just as they were written by Moses in the Old Testament.

"Now, just another jewel or two, and we shall really have to finish for tonight. There is another famous topaz in the nineteenth psalm—you know, where we found so many of them before. This one is in verse 7."

Doreen found the verse and read, " 'The law of the Lord is perfect, converting the soul.' "

"The more we think about God's perfect law, and His thoughtfulness in giving every commandment for our good always," said Mamma, "the more our hearts will be drawn to love Him.

"And now for that beautiful opal to finish off our locket. It is found in Psalm 119:10. Don't bother to look it up, for you must be tired. It runs like this: 'O let me not wander from Thy commandments.' That is another beautiful prayer for us to remember and to use from day to day. If only we could be kept from wandering from His commandments, how happy we should always be!"

"That makes six jewels we have put into our golden locket," said Doreen.

"Yes," said Mamma, "and I hope they have not only been put into a heart-shaped locket, but also into the more precious locket of our hearts."

176

DOREEN'S JEWEL BOX

A Necklace of Sympathy

Isn't it dreadfully sad?" said Doreen, bursting into the house on her return from school. "Little Joan Whittaker is dead."

"Oh, my dear, no!" exclaimed Mother. "How did it happen?"

"She was run over this afternoon by a truck on High Street."

"Those dreadful trucks!" said Mamma. "I must run around to Mrs. Whittaker's at once."

That night they could hardly begin making their Bible jewelry for talking about the sad accident and all the sorrow it had brought into the Whittaker home.

4-12

"If we make anything tonight," said Mamma, "it must be a necklace of sympathy for poor Mrs. Whittaker. She is brokenhearted. Shall we try to find some precious jewels for her, and send them to her tomorrow?"

"That is a lovely idea, Mamma," said Doreen. "We must try hard to find the very best there are."

"I know one that I want to put in first of all," said Mamma. "It is a wonderful amethyst in the last chapter of Isaiah, and reads like this: 'As one whom his mother comforteth, so will I comfort you.' Verse 13."

"How do you think of such beautiful verses so easily?" asked Doreen.

178

"Ah, we must know them so well that we can think of them any time we need them," said Mamma. "Here is another jewel that is just what we want: 'Comfort ye, comfort ye My people.' Isaiah 40:1. Can't you see Jesus bending over some-one with tear-stained eyes, whispering these beautiful words? They sound like a Mother saying, 'Don't cry any more, it will soon be all right again.' "

"Yes, isn't it just like that!" said Doreen.

"And that reminds me of another jewel—a topaz this time —that we must set in our necklace of sympathy. You will discover it in the first book of Thessalonians."

"The book that's so hard for me to find," interrupted Doreen.

"Not so very hard," said Mamma. "Look it up, dear. It's in the fourth chapter."

"Do you mean verse 17?"

"No, begin with verse 16, where it says: 'The Lord Himself.' "

"I see. 'The Lord Himself shall descend from heaven with a shout, with the voice of the Archangel, and with the trump of God: and the dead in Christ shall rise first: then we which are alive and remain shall be caught up together with them in the clouds, to meet the Lord in the air: and so shall we ever be with the Lord.' "

"Read the next verse as well," said Mamma.

Doreen did so. " 'Wherefore comfort one another with these words.' "

"See how the 'comfort' comes in again," said Mamma. "Jesus does not want His people ever to be oversorrowful, not even when their loved ones die. He tells us that He will

179

surely come back someday and bring all the dead to
life again. Little Joan will live again when Jesus comes,
and her mamma will see her once more."

"One of the girls told me that Joan had gone to heaven,"
said Doreen.

"Oh, no. Many people think that, but the Bible does not
say so. When people die, they do not know anything, and
will not, until Jesus comes back to make them alive again. 'The
dead know not any thing.' Ecclesiastes 9:5. They just go into
a deep, deep sleep."

"But what a long, long time to sleep!" said Doreen.

"Not so long as you think," said Mamma. "When you are

180

asleep you do not notice how time is passing. In the morning it seems like just a moment since you went to bed. So it will be with little Joan. When she was crossing High Street, she was probably thinking of getting home quickly and kissing her mamma and having her supper. Then that terrible big truck came along and knocked her over. The next moment— to her—she will see Jesus coming back in all His glory, and the angels will take her to her mother, and it will seem just as if she were going home to supper after all."

"How beautiful!" said Doreen. "And won't they be happy to see each other again!"

"They will, indeed," said Mamma. "And that's why I want to put these jewels in our necklace for Mrs. Whittaker.

But we must have some more. There is a very precious opal in the first book of Corinthians."

"Which chapter?" asked Doreen, turning to the New Testament.

"Chapter 15, verse 55."

Doreen read the familiar words: " 'O death, where is thy sting? O grave, where is thy victory?' "

"The sting is taken out of death," said Mamma, "by the knowledge that Jesus is coming back again to make the dead alive. So we must put that jewel in the necklace. And we mustn't leave out that other precious amethyst in Revelation 21, verse 4: 'And God shall wipe away all tears.' Do read it all, Doreen."

Doreen turned to the verse and read, " 'And God shall wipe away all tears from their eyes; and there shall be no more death, neither sorrow, nor crying, neither shall there be any more pain: for the former things are passed away.' "

"Oh, we must put that in!" said Doreen.

"Yes," said Mamma, "and what a wonderful picture it gives us! It tells us that God will come close enough to all His sorrowing children to put His arms around them and wipe their tears away. It helps us to see how much He loves us and how He understands. True, the verse speaks of heaven and the New Jerusalem, where there shall be no more death or pain or sorrow, but I am sure it means also that God is waiting to comfort us now, whenever we feel sad."

"If Mrs. Whittaker will look at this precious necklace, I am sure it will make her feel happier," said Doreen.

"I'm sure it will," said Mamma. "But there is one more jewel I want to put into it. It is a bright-red ruby of hope.

182

You will find it tucked away in the book of Jeremiah. It is in chapter 31, verses 16 and 17."

Doreen turned to the place and read, " 'Refrain thy voice from weeping, and thine eyes from tears: for thy work shall be rewarded, saith the Lord; and they shall come again from the land of the enemy. And there is hope in thine end, saith the Lord, that thy children shall come again.'

"Doesn't that fit exactly!" she said.

"Indeed it does," said Mamma, "and it will take to Mrs. Whittaker a definite message from Jesus that 'there is hope' that dear little Joan will come back again. I think she will be so pleased to know of this precious promise."

"Yes," said Doreen, "what a beautiful necklace of sympathy we have made tonight!"

A Coronet of Hope

I have been thinking a good deal today," said Mamma, "about that necklace of sympathy we made last night, and I want to make another piece of jewelry to go with it. We have now made a prayer bracelet, a locket of love, and a necklace of sympathy. Let us crown them all with a coronet of hope."

"That sounds lovely," said Doreen. "Let us start on it right away. We must have some extra-special jewels for a coronet."

"We shall," said Mamma. "Do you remember how long ago it was that Jesus lived on the earth?"

185

sus, the children's Friend, promised to come again, and He has never broken a promise.

"I'm afraid I don't."

"Well, more than nineteen hundred years. That is a very long time. And if it were not for the story in the Bible, most people would have forgotten all about Him by now. But here we have the story of His wonderful life, and it has made us fall in love with Him. He was so kind and good and noble that we cannot help loving Him. His heroic death on the cruel cross only makes us love Him all the more. His rising from the dead afterward, and His going up into heaven, were also very wonderful, and lead us to worship Him. But the best thing about Jesus is that He is still living today, waiting to come back to this world."

"How old He must be!" said Doreen.

"Truly, the years have passed," said Mamma, "but I don't think that Jesus will ever grow old. Life is different in heaven. 'There is no night there'—no disease, no death, and the passing of time only makes those who live there more wise and beautiful. And that brings me to the first jewel for our coronet

186

of hope. It is an amethyst, and you will find it in John 14, verse 3."

Doreen read, " 'And if I go and prepare a place for you, I will come again, and receive you unto Myself; that where I am, there ye may be also.' "

"There we have the definite promise of Jesus," said Mamma, "that He will indeed return someday. He has been a long time coming, but as long as that verse is there, we may have hope that He will come back. But now add a topaz to our coronet. It is in the first chapter of Acts, verse 11."

Again Doreen eagerly turned the pages of her Bible, and read the words: " 'This same Jesus, which is taken up from you into heaven, shall so come in like manner as ye have seen Him go into heaven.' "

"This promise is to strengthen our hope," said Mamma. "It tells us not only that He will return, but that He will come back just the same as He went away. He will not have changed. His disciples will recognize Him at once. He will be just the same loving, friendly, helpful Saviour that He was in the old days."

"But shall we see Him coming down through the sky?" asked Doreen.

"Of course we shall,"
said Mamma. "Just as the
disciples saw Him go away,
so we shall see Him come back.
'Every eye shall see Him,' we
are told. Revelation 1:7. And that
is a wonderful emerald for our coronet, isn't it? But Jesus Himself said
that He would come back in full view
of everyone on earth: 'As the lightning
cometh out of the east, and shineth even
unto the west; so shall also the coming
of the Son of man be.' Matthew 24:27."

"And that's an amethyst for the coronet," said Doreen.

188

"Yes, dear, and there's a jasper in Matthew 26, verse 64, that we may add as well: 'Jesus saith unto him [the high priest], . . . Hereafter shall ye see the Son of man sitting on the right hand of power, and coming in the clouds of heaven.' So there is no doubt about our seeing Him when He comes. And we shall hear Him, too, for there is that onyx we found the other night: 'Our God shall come, and shall not keep silence.' Psalm 50:3. And there's that other topaz we found, too: 'The Lord Himself shall descend from heaven with a shout, with the voice of the Archangel, and with the trump of God.' So, dearie, we shall both see Him and hear Him when He comes. There is no danger of His coming secretly and some of us not knowing anything about it."

"But I think it will be very terrible when He does come," said Doreen. "I am afraid I shall be very much frightened."

"There is no need to be frightened," said Mamma. "You wouldn't be frightened if you knew that your best school friend was coming to supper tomorrow night, would you?"

"Of course not," said Doreen.

"Well, it's much the same. Jesus is the best friend we have, and we should be looking forward to the day when He will come back to this earth. So long as we keep friends with Him, we need not fear His coming."

"But what about the bad people who don't love Him?" asked Doreen.

"They will be very sorry for themselves," said Mamma. "Isaiah tells us that they will go 'into the holes of the rocks, and into the caves of the earth, for fear of the Lord, and for the glory of His majesty, when He ariseth to shake terribly the earth.' Isaiah 2:19. It certainly will be a terrible day for

them. But we do not need to think about that. If we just keep on loving Him a little more every day, we may be quite sure that He will take care of us when He comes."

"And what will happen after that?" asked Doreen.

"After that? Well, then we shall go back with Him to heaven. And after that, when He has made the earth all beautiful again, like the Garden of Eden, He will bring us here

once more, and we shall live in a beautiful home by the river of life forever and ever. We shall be so happy then. As we read last night, 'there shall be no more death, neither sorrow, nor crying, neither shall there be any more pain.' No more toothaches, dearie, no more headaches, no more heartaches. No more dreadful accidents, no more war, no more tears. Oh, it is a glorious home that Jesus is preparing for us! And that reminds me, do find that beautiful topaz in the eleventh chapter of Isaiah."

Doreen turned to the chapter and read the sixth verse: " 'The wolf also shall dwell with the lamb, and the leopard shall lie down with the kid; and the calf and the young lion and the fatling together; and a little child shall lead them.' "

"What a wonderful picture of peace!" said Mamma. "Even the ani-

191

mals will have stopped trying to kill one another, and will lie down together in friendliness and safety. Best of all, 'a little child shall lead them.' I am so glad Jesus has told us that He has a place in His beautiful home for children. He never forgets the children, Doreen, dear. He wants them to be with Him there."

"It makes me want to go and see it all now," said Doreen.

"We can't do that," said Mamma, "but we can hope and pray that He will come soon and take us there. Now let us add just two more jewels to make our coronet complete. The first is a sapphire, and is a message from Jesus Himself. You will find it in the last chapter of the Bible, almost the last verse."

Doreen soon found it and read the familiar words: " 'Surely I come quickly.' "

"And now give us that glorious emerald that follows it," said Mamma.

"I see it," said Doreen. "It is in the same verse: 'Even so, come, Lord Jesus.' "

"What a beautiful coronet of hope all these jewels have made for us!" said Mamma. "We must wear it on our foreheads every day, and let everybody know that we are longing for Jesus to come back soon."

"Yes," said Doreen, "and what with bracelets and lockets and coronets, this has turned out to be a wonderful jewel box, after all, hasn't it, Mamma?"

"You are right," said Mamma. "It is the richest treasure chest in all the world."